The Divinity WITHIN

A 12-Month Journal: Daily Routines to Transform Your Body, Mind, and Spirit with Ayurveda and Yoga

Dr. Z. Light Miller ¤ Batool Merali

The Divinity Within

Art Director: Batool Merali
Front Cover, Print & E-book Book Design: Idafiasveningsson.se
Editors: Frannie Ferrara, Spencer Hamilton
Proof Readers: Spencer Hamilton from Nerdy Wordsmith Ink, Michelle Cornish
Many thanks to the Production Artists: Sunil Kargwal, Velin Perseus, Jyotsna Ramachandran, and Lissa Sandler

ISBN: 978-0-9988160-0-5
Digital edition published in 2017 eISBN: 978-0-9988160-1-2

Library of Congress Cataloging-in-Publication data available

DISCLAIMER

The information provided in this journal is for informational purposes only and is not intended to serve as a substitute for medical advice, diagnosis, treatment, or prescribing. Nothing contained in this journal should be considered to be medical advice, diagnosis, treatment, or prescribing, a promise of benefits, claim of cure, or guarantee of results to be achieved. The authors are not medical doctors. Consult with a licensed healthcare professional before altering or discontinuing any current medications, treatment or care, or starting any diet, exercise or supplementation program, or if you have or suspect you may have a health condition that requires medical attention. Check with your doctor before taking herbs or using essential oils, especially when pregnant or nursing. The United States Food and Drug Administration (USFDA) has not evaluated any statement, claim, or representation made in this journal.

Printed in United States of America
Nourish Communications

WWW.AYURVEDICHEALERS.COM | WWW.NOURISHMYSELF.COM

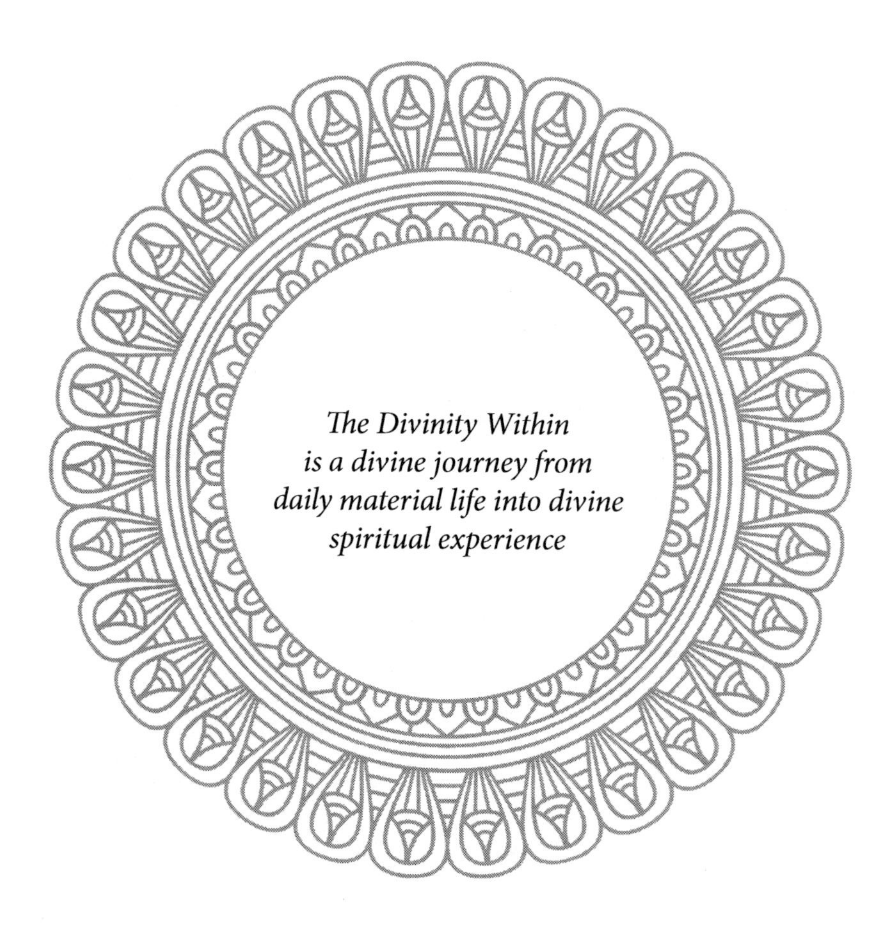

The Divinity Within
is a divine journey from
daily material life into divine
spiritual experience

– DR. VASANT LAD –

BAM&S, MASc, Ayurvedic Physician

Author of Ayurveda: Science of Self-Healing, Textbook of Ayurveda series and more.

WHAT PEOPLE ARE SAYING ABOUT THE DIVINITY WITHIN

“

The Divinity Within journal is a tool for transformation, allowing us to have an evolutionary experience of our own making as we meet each day with choices to evolve in body, mind, and spirit, using time-tested techniques of mantra, breath, yoga, food, herbs, and reflective insight as a way to participate in our highest alignment.

— BRIGITTE MARS
Author of The Country Almanac of Home Remedies, The Desktop Guide to Herbal Medicine
www.brigittemars.com

The Divinity Within is an excellent tool for personal health and well-being. Batool Merali and Light Miller have done a wonderful job in creating a wonderful template for daily living. It will inspire, motivate, and simply cultivate a healthy attitude for a spiritual life. It is a one-year challenge that will add many more quality years to your life.

— DR. SUHAS KSHIRSAGAR
Author, Ayurvedic Physician. | www.AyurvedicHealing.Net

This book is the first of its kind: a comprehensive Dinacharya Journal for those committed to living a lifestyle in harmony with ayurvedic principles.

— DR. SHEKHAR ANNAMBHOTLA
President, Association of Ayurvedic Professionals of North America (AAPNA)

Journaling is an important way to focus the mind and transform consciousness. *The Divinity Within* gives the reader the opportunity to focus on the daily practices of Ayurveda as a transformative tool. Where there is harmony, there is health. Where there is disharmony, there is disease. This journal provides a structure to assist the reader in creating a life of harmony, which will most certainly bear the sweetest of fruits.

— DR. MARC HALPERN (DR.SHIVA)
President: California College of Ayurveda
Author: Healing Your Life; Lessons on the Path of Ayurveda
Author: Recording; Yoga Nidra and Self Healing

“

The beauty of the journal is in its simplicity and structure. With the vast science of Ayurveda, its foundation is based on creating a routine that allows the healing process to occur. *The Divinty Within* journal allows each individual to be guided using daily goals, checklists, calendars to track progress, blended with knowledge on deities, mudras, chakras and essential oils to create accountability and opportunity for expansion and growth.

— TRUPTI GOKANI, MD
Board-Certified Neurologist, Ayurvedic Expert
Author of *The Mysterious Mind: How to Use Ancient Wisdom and Modern Science to Heal your Headaches and Reclaim your Health*

The Divinity Within journal is a delightful and practical tool for anyone looking to learn Ayurveda through taking their own day-to-day life into their own hands. Batool and Light will help you tap into your inner radiance and learn how to polish your light to glow through your life.

— CATE STILLMAN
Founder + podcast host @ www.yogahealer.com
Author of *Body Thrive.*

The Divinity Within journal offers anyone on a journey of self-discovery and transformation a beautiful way to cultivate mindfulness and add awareness to the days, weeks, seasons and year ahead. Students of Ayurveda will find it a particularly helpful tool for establishing their dinacharya, daily routine.

— UMĀ JOLICOEUR
Curriculum & Seminar Coordinator, Faculty | The Ayurvedic Institute

Ayurveda is the science of life. Life is a daily practice. At its best it is moving toward mindfulness and intelligence, infusing our thoughts and subsequent actions—especially in those daily activities that keep us healthy, alert, and content. Ayurveda is also a compendium of thousands of years of wisdom that can be translated into these daily practices to help with diet, lifestyle, and steadying routines. To have a journal to see us through this sea of change in our behavior is to actualize this wisdom. Thus the results can be measured and shown to validate our direction toward intelligence and health. I commend the authors for presenting this wisdom in such a clear and practical manner.

— ARUN DEVA
AP-NAMA, AYT, E-RYT500, Arunachala Yoga & Ayurveda
Ayurvedic Facilitator of Awakenings, Seeker of the Buddha in every face.

“

The Divinty Within mirrors the unfolding loveliness found in yoga and Ayurveda. This is not for yogis only but a quest for self-knowledge with an opening and loving heart. Join the authors in seeking wellness, ease, health, and love with practical tips that bring personal change within reach of us all.

— NOAH MAZE

Founder of YOGAMAZÉ | www.yogamaze.net

The Divinity Within journal is a unique tool for positively transforming your life. Not only does it share ancient life-enhancing knowledge and techniques, it also shows you step-by-step how to integrate this knowledge into your everyday life. It is a must-have for serious yoga practitioners, as well as those just beginning down the Vedic path.

— SUSAN ETHERIDGE

Ayurvedic Practitioner, Yoga Teacher, and Alternative Health Lawyer

What a beautiful book!! It's the perfect resource for *anyone* to use as they journal their way to their own goals while tuning in to the ancient wisdom of Ayurveda. I can't wait to share this book with my family, friends, and students. A true gift!

— SHELLY AARON

Health & Fitness Coach | Rejuveclub.com

To begin reading and writing in this journal is to bring a luminous, liberating clarity to your life. *The Divinity Within* journal is an inspiring, joyful reminder we all need at this pivotal moment that ultimate fulfillment of the divine journey is love. It's simple, fun, and playful. The easy-to-follow format blending Ayurveda with the Habit Tracker is brilliant. We are extremely fortunate to have this beautiful journal bringing sacredness into our daily routines.

— SARAH O'NEIL

Certified Yoga Health Coach | www.simplewellnessnow.net

I am very proud of my girls Batool and Jyoti. This book takes me back to my childhood and the simple and effective home remedies my parents and grandparents used, and which I have carried on in my family. We seem to have come back a full circle to the intelligence and wisdom of our forefathers that have given us health, longevity, and satisfaction.

— ZEENAT (NANI)

Mother, grandmother, great-grandma, great-great-grandma

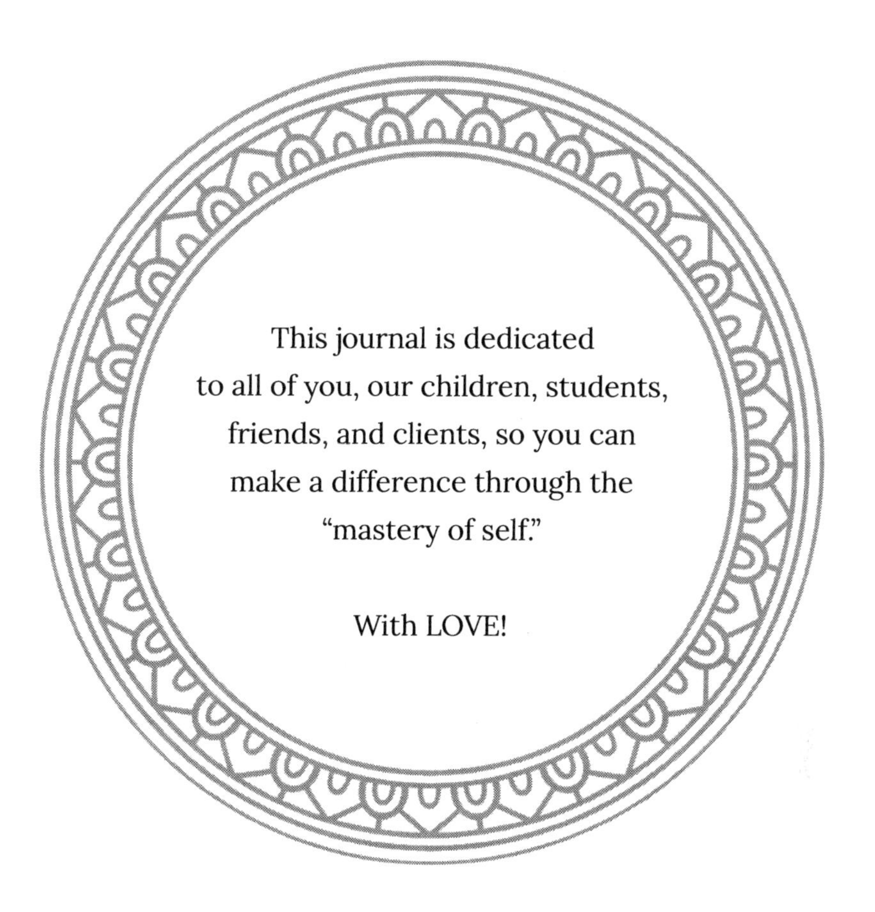

— LIGHT & BATOOL —

THIS JOURNAL BELONGS TO

NAME

ADDRESS

TELEPHONE

EMAIL

"

If you want to change the world,
start with yourself.

— MAHATMA GANDHI —

FOREWORD

"*You hold in your hands a notebook like no other from the expert team of Dr. Light Miller and Batool Merali, who have shared decades of wisdom in the works. This fascinating Ayurveda journal brings alive awe-inspiring gems from the sacred core of the Ayurvedas to open your own divinity. With a wealth of helpful lessons, archetypal stories, and tips, this journal is a conscious companion, your definitive guru that can hold your hands and guide you through challenges amid your daily course. The emphasis in this unusual journal is that through sacred everyday practice we are apt to stay centered in the moment-to-moment awareness that is continually revealing who we truly are. At its core, a blissful experience can be had by all who drink from its visionary well. Be happy, journal well.*

— MAYA TIWARI —

Ayurveda Pioneer & Humanitarian

“ I believe that I came to this earth to master myself and to return to my true self. For over 25 years, I have used journals to keep track of my vision and my spiritual journey. Journals have been the tools that I use to discover my purpose in life (dharma) and actualize my goals. It is the way that I have contributed to the world as a healer, writer, and to serve my clients. This has allowed my soul full expression and allowed me to visualize my goals, release my attachments, and allow divine timing to take place in my life. It has also given me an opportunity to examine my motives, mobilize my intelligence, and work with my daily challenges, always seeing the bigger picture.

Karma is cause and effect. We can create it, burn it off, or complete it. Each goal attained allows me to be in gratitude. In my journaling, I always set to bring forth the attributes of deities, angels, saints, and people who I want to mentor me, especially yogis and beings of great wisdom. Ayurveda, yoga, and mantra have helped me channel the journey into sacredness into my consciousness. I use the journal approach to explore and ground myself in life's specifics. "What" and "when" compose a goal. It takes vigilance, discipline, practice, and commitment to turn dreams into reality. One can become the observer of how we live our life and learn by watching self.

I invite you to use this journal to find your place in the spiritual, mental, and physical realms. The manifestation of what you came to accomplish and sharing it with others is your birthright. Through your gift, it is possible for us to heal our self, our families, our community, the nation, and the planet. Let's make big dreams of peace, love, and joy.

Hari OM Tat Sat (*The 3 aspects of GOD are within me*).

— LIGHT MILLER —

“ Who am I? Who do I want to become?

To answer these questions, to really engage in my own becoming, I knew I had to document my day-to-day activities, emotions, thoughts, fears, and desires. And, in turn, by documenting and staying mindful of these moments, I would walk a path reconnecting with my heart, body, and soul. In today's culture, we live with the general philosophy that we need to consume more, have more, buy more, and do more without considering the impact on ourselves, our families, our communities, and our planet.

Troubled by this, and in need of guidance, I turned within looking for an Avatar. I found the scriptures of ancient India, filled with the stories of gods and goddesses—our divine avatars. These scriptures entwined philosophy with devotion, allowing me to focus on the divine within. By connecting with these divine avatars, I was able to not only pay homage to the enlightened guru that resides within but also find the tools to counter my disconnection. By taking a deeper dive into the day-to-day, moment-to-moment activities, I could access the energy of the divine within and allow this energy to guide me. Using all the tools from my toolbox, I was on a path to heal life's mystery.

This journal is designed to put you on a path of self-discovery and inquiry, one that grounds your understanding of "self" through Ayurveda and yoga. Through these sciences you will understand how your dosha—energetic makeup—affects the entirety of your being. How your dinacharya—your daily routine and habits support your health and transformation.

I am forever grateful to ***all*** *my teachers for helping me achieve my clear path. My heartfelt thanks to my family, friends, and teachers for your support and love.*

Dr. Vasant Lad for being my guruji, helping me secure the title of this journal, and all the valuable wisdom you share.

Dr. Light Miller for your immense knowledge, commitment to help humanity, guiding passion, friendship, and trust.

From my heart to yours, a deep bow,

— BATOOL —

MAHAMRITYUNJAYA MANTRA

[*MAHA-MRITYUN-JAYA*]

"MOKSHA MANTRA"

The maha mrityunjaya mantra helps us tune into the healing force that is always at work within us, supporting our growth, lifting our spirits in times of trouble, and reminding us of the higher purpose of life.

OM TRYAMBAKAM YAJAMAHE
We meditate on the three-eyed reality,

SUGANDHIM PUSHTI-VARDHANAM
Which permeates and nourishes all like a fragrance.

URVARUKAMIVA BANDHANAN
May we be liberated from death for the sake of imortality,

MRITYOR MUKSHIYA MAMRITAT
Even as the cucumber is severed from bondage to the creeper.

WHAT IS AYURVEDA?

The concept of the interconnectivity of our mind, body, and spirit is not a modern creation. This paradigm was discovered and interpreted in the subcontinent of ancient India thousands of years ago. It is believed that there is harmony in all elements in our Universe.

Ayurveda (*ah-yer-vey-duh*) is a Sanskrit word that translates to mean the science of life—*ayur* meaning life and veda meaning science or knowledge. It is a holistic practice of restoring the essential connectivity of the satva (mind), sharira (body), and atma (spirit) in order to function as one harmonious entity known as man or purusha.

The practice of Ayurveda comes from the Samkhya, a Hindu system of cosmology. According to Samkhya, man (prusha) and female (prakruti) unite to produce cosmic intelligence. Prakruti and Prusha reveal the three modes of nature called gunas. The gunas give rise to three principles —satva, rajas, and tamas. Satva represents intelligence, awakening, and balance. Rajas is the energy of movement which can cause imbalance. Tamas is darkness which can create inertia and ignorance. These three principles form the foundation of all existence and are contained in balance in Prakruti.

Satva creates the organic universe and tamas creates the inorganic universe, while rajas is the active force that moves these universes. An essential role of tamas is creating our five sensory perceptions—sound, touch, taste, smell, and sight. These five senses produce the five key elements of creation—water, fire, earth, ether, and air.

The elements exist in varying proportions in all forms of matter including plants, animals, and the human body and combine to form three distinct energies or doshas—vata, pitta, and kapha. Vata is made of air and ether. Pitta combines fire and water. Kapha is water and earth. The goal of Ayurveda is to strike a balance among the doshas for a healthier mind, body, and spirit. We find this balance through diet, exercise, and healthy living.

Understanding the interactions of our doshas leads us to the path of balance and healing. As we find this balance, we create a paradigm of healing that spreads from us to friends and family, to whole neighborhoods and communities, until there is a societal shift in attitude towards good health instead of being at war with our bodies. When the collective consciousness changes to one of healing and self-responsibility, we will all experience lives of fulfillment and harmony within our society.

It is said that planetary healing takes place one life at a time. Ayurveda helps us take the first step towards this grand universal goal.

INTRODUCTION

The journal in your hand was created for those who want to live a life of balance and bliss. You can use these pages to track your path to self discovery, mastery, and creation. Allow this to become your daily ritual for 365 days.

You are on the path to discovering the truth—that life is a sacred journey and often we live in forgetfulness. By nourishing ourselves with the gifts of nature and living our Dharma (purpose), we uncover our true path. When we practice Ayurveda, we begin to burn our Karma (actions) and start our path toward enlightenment.

Reading the sacred teachings of yoga and Ayurveda will teach you valuable wisdom—we come to this earth in a journey to find our way back to a higher being. Through these teachings, we join our mind, body, and spirit into the omnipresence of the infinite power of the divine within.

We should practice forgiveness, truth, detachment, and cleanliness of thought as we live in accordance with what is right and create a life based on love and compassion. We live by the laws of nature because what is pure and natural is closer to the divine.

Through meditation, affirmations, mantra, self-observation, and rituals, the divine voice speaks to us as it has spoken to many enlightened beings. Incorporating prayer, yoga, exercise, good food, tai chi, chi gong, and Ayurveda will help in this journey. Observe that when you write about these areas of your life, you are clearing your path to spiritual awakening. Seeing your activities noted down on a daily basis, your consciousness begins to unfold and you reach a greater understanding of who you are. Your journey, paths, dreams, and visions become clear.

This journal offers stories of divine beings through the ages. They show us how to bring forth the true essence of our being. Whatever we think and believe becomes a reality when we practice a life of devotion and awaken the light within.

Committing to this journal is an opportunity to develop your divine attributes through daily interactions with the world around you. The stories, mantras, and mudras show you how to give love to yourself, your family, your community, your nation, and finally, your mother planet.

Each day of this disciplined journaling practice, you will observe a shift taking place, and passion for life will grow inside you. You will learn how to transform challenges into opportunities which in turn will help you embrace empowerment.

Use this journal to find clarity and peace in your mind and spirit. This is not created to show off or to beat ourselves up but rather to write down what we want to become since we have been bestowed free will. Through this personal record of your life, you can discover the gift that you are to yourself.

This is what we came here to do. We were taught by all the ancient religions and civilizations of the world that we will return to the realm of divinity through our journey in life, but we have merely forgotten. Today, let's remember this transcendental wisdom. Turn the pages of your journal, be the author of your own story ... and discover where the path of enlightenment will take you.

LET THE JOURNEY BEGIN

This journal of self-discovery and personal development is designed to help you reach elevated heights in your mental, emotional, and physical wellbeing. It is designed to help you meet your goals and manifest your desired outcomes by giving you a structure to tap into the tools of Ayurveda and yoga. As you move through the days and work with this journal, trust the process. Be kind to yourself. Small steps will lead to big changes. Build the foundation that will let you live your dreams and live life to its fullest.

HAVE A *VISION*

Create a vision board for yourself. A vision board is a tool used to help you clarify, concentrate, and maintain focus on specific life goals. Having pictures, images, and sayings helps manifest your dreams into reality.

PICK A *DIVINE AVATAR*

Connect with a deity presented in these pages or find your own. Let these divine beings guide you in conquering and manifesting your own desires.

CREATE *SPACE*

Create a clear space where you can experience a depth of peace, richness, and sense of meaning. Remember this space includes the largeness of all your being—your thoughts, emotions, home, friends, family, etc. Start where it feels right to you and allow your intuition to guide you.

MEDITATE

Sit in silence. Silence calms the mind and converts negative thoughts into positive affirmations. Meditation gives clarity, reduces stress, and helps you get more focused.

CHOOSE A *MANTRA*

Find a mantra that resonates with you, and repeat it often. When chanting your mantra, you bypass the mind and connect to the heart. Beeja mantra is one syllable, a seed or vibration for the soul.

EXPLORE *MUDRAS* AND *YANTRAS*

Mudras are hand gestures used during meditation, pranayama, and yoga to direct the flow of energy. The position of the hands influences the energy of our physical, emotional, and spiritual body. This energy is a link between the individual pranic force and the universal cosmic energy.

Yantras are visual tools that serve in meditation either as centering devices or as symbolic compositions of the energy patterns.

ASANAS—*YOGA POSES*

These are physical postures that connect breath and movement, mind and body. Each month an asana has been highlighted according to the season and its corresponding dosha to promote balance and wellbeing.

FOCUS WITH A *DRISHTI*

By focusing your gaze on a drishti—either an external focal point or the internal focal point of your third eye—you allow the mind to move into a state of deep concentration.

TAP INTO *PRANAYAMA*

We often forget to breathe consciously. Pranayama breathing techniques help increase the oxygen supply to the brain while relaxing the mind and body. Explore the different techniques—nadi sodhan, ujjayi, bhastrika, bhramari, so hum—to calm you, help you focus, kindle the fire, or heat you up.

DISCOVER YOUR *DOSHA*

The doshas—*vata*, *pitta*, and *kappa*—are biological energies found throughout the human body and mind. They govern all physical and mental processes and provide every living being with an individual blueprint for health and fulfillment. The doshas are derived from the five elements—ether, air, fire, water, earth.

FIND BALANCE THROUGH *FOOD*

According to Ayurveda, when we're balanced, we desire foods that are good for us. But when our mind, body, or spirit is out of sync, our connection to our body's inner intelligence is lost.

BUILD YOUR *DINACHARYA—DAILY ROUTINE*

A consistent daily routine—dinacharya—allows the body to be in tune with the cycles of nature, the circadian clock promoting optimal health and wellness. This routine keeps the body and its mechanics in tune with the cycles of the three doshas, which are dominant at the following times of day:

- KAPHA: 6:00AM - 10:00AM AND 6:00PM - 10:00PM
- PITTA: 10:00AM - 2:00PM AND 10:00PM - 2:00AM
- VATA: 2:00PM - 6:00PM AND 2:00AM - 6:00AM

DEVELOP STRONG *HABITS*

Let your dinacharya evolve into a habitual behavioral pattern, one that is easeful, second-nature, and completely automatic.

FOLLOW THE AYURVEDIC CLOCK

It is a tool to align our lives to natural rhythms. Living in sync with nature's rhythms brings harmony and balance to the mind and body. It is a way to put our life into perspective. Wake up when the sun rises and slow down when the sun sets. Eat your biggest meal in the middle of the day when the heat is high and the digestive system is at its peak. Certain hours of the day correspond to certain organs in the body. Following the natural rhythms of our own body enhances health. Going against the natural rhythms causes disruption in our health.

AYURVEDIC CHECKLIST

Make sure you document your daily activities.

GOAL & HABIT TRACKER

In order to notice change and live your dreams, keep yourself accountable by tracking your progress.

LEAN INTO YOUR *SENSES*

Engage your sense of smell with *essential oils*. The aromatic essence from plants balances, harmonizes, and promotes the health of body, mind, and spirit.

Explore your kitchen pharmacy by connecting with your sense of taste through *herbs and spices* to cure digestive issues, colds, congestion, and to build your immune system.

CONNECT

Be kind to yourself—you are not alone. Find an accountability partner. Host a vision board party. Let's all help each other, our family, our planet, and the Universe.

And reach out to us!

We'd love to hear from you and support you on your journey.

We wish you the very best.

@ZLIGHT & @BATOOL_NOURISHMYSELF

WWW.AYURVEDICHEALERS.COM | WWW.NOURISHMYSELF.COM

MY VISION PLAN FOR THE YEAR

Please draw, illustrate, write, or paste pictures of the vision, purpose, growth, and accomplishments you wish to manifest for the year.

JANUARY

BRAHMA

(God of Creation)

Lord Brahma is the creator of all beings and the entire Universe. He is part of the Trimurti (Hindu Trinity), along with Vishnu and Shiva. He is the guardian of the Vedas, the most ancient and Holy Scriptures. The Puranas state that Brahma is the Son of God and was self-born out of a lotus flower which grew from the navel of Lord Vishnu.

Brahma resides in Brahmaloka, the highest world within the material worlds. His wife, Saraswati, is the Goddess of Knowledge, Music, and Arts. Lord Brahma governs the day and night cycles of the Universe. His life is calculated to be one hundred years, after which he is reborn and the whole creation begins anew.

Brahma is depicted as a four-faced God seated on a lotus flower in Padmasana, or the lotus pose. He has a long white beard, and each of his heads is reciting the four Vedas. His skin is red and he has four arms, each holding a sacred object: a water-pot (Kamandalu), a manuscript (Vedas), a sacrificial implement (Sruva), and a rosary or, sometimes, a lotus flower (Mala). Lord Brahma moves around on a white swan.

He is mostly worshiped as part of the trinity, very rarely is he worshiped individually. You can call on Lord Brahma to guide you in your new journey for the year.

MANTRA

SOUND

"Gurubrahma Guruvishnu Gurudevo Maheswarah, Guru saakshaat Param Brahma Tasmai shri guravey Namaha."

MEANING

Lord Brahma the Creator is the teacher and is supreme amongst all other Gods. He is verily Lord Vishnu and Lord Shiva Himself. I offer my salutations.

BIJA MANTRA: *AUM*

JANUARY

MON	TUE	WED	THU	FRI	SAT	SUN
					Emotional Breakdown 6	
	★ If you're hitting your head against a wall... walk around the wall. (try 10 minutes a day on what's present. Let the other stuff rest.) 8				(little boy w/ clock in pieces)	

MY GOALS

PERSONAL

ACTION STEPS

SPIRITUAL

ACTION STEPS

CAREER

ACTION STEPS

TOOLS AND TASKS FOR JANUARY

Explore the healing power of yantras, herbs/spices, oils, yoga postures, and habits. Feel the effects on the body, mind, and spirit. Write down how they connect to your divine life.

HERB/SPICE
Basil

HABIT
Mindfulness
meditation
pranayama

OIL
Tulsi

YOGA POSE
Tree Pose
Vrksasana

WRITE YOUR ACCOMPLISHMENTS FOR THE MONTH

VICTORIES

ENLIGHTENED EXPERIENCE

REWARD

WHAT DID NOT HAPPEN AND WHY?

MONTHLY REVIEW

DID I ACCOMPLISH ALL
MY GOALS FOR THE MONTH?

MY TOP 3 ACCOMPLISHMENTS
FOR THE MONTH

MY TOP 3 CHALLENGES
FOR THE MONTH

WERE MY ACTIONS IN ALIGNMENT
WITH WHO I ASPIRE TO BE?

I AM THANKFUL FOR

WHAT MAKES ME HAPPY?

“

If your eyes are blinded with your worries,
you cannot see the beauty of the sunset.

– KRISHNAMURTI

BLESSINGS AND GRATITUDE

AFFIRMATIONS

FEBRUARY

RADHA AND KRISHNA

(God of Love, Knowledge, and Beauty)
(Goddess of Love, Power, and Kindness)

Radharani and Lord Krishna are the symbols of divine love beyond words. They are a combination of the feminine and masculine powers of God. Krishna is considered Svayam Bhagavan, or *Supreme God Himself*, and is the source of all incarnations; Radha Rani is his consort and beloved. They both reside in Goloka, the supreme heaven.

Lord Krishna is dark in color. He wears a crown with a peacock feather called a Mormukut and a yellow-colored dress known as the Peetambar. A garland of rare flowers called the Vaijayanti Mala adorns his neck. His ornaments are intricate with many precious jewels. Standing cross-legged, his head is always bent toward his beloved Radha Rani.

Radha Rani possesses unmatched beauty and fair complexion. She is the epitome of love and grace. She dons a blue-colored dress and her head is always covered with a veil. She wears exquisite jewelry, which augments her beauty while she stands gracefully next to her beloved Shree Krishna.

Lord Krishna in Vrindavana is mostly depicted with Radha standing on his left. He holds her with one hand and a flute in the other. Radha Rani is considered as the soul of Shri Krishna.

Let their sacred union inspire you to embrace unconditional love in your life.

MANTRA

SOUND

"Hare Krishna, Hare Krishna, Krishna Krishna, Hare Hare, Hare Rama, Hare Rama, Rama Rama, Hare Hare."

MEANING

Radha is in Krishna's love; and Krishna or Hari is in Radha's love. The only dependable wealth in life is Radha and Krishna, and in them I take refuge.

BIJA MANTRA: *KLIM*

FEBRUARY

MON	TUE	WED	THU	FRI	SAT	SUN

MY GOALS

PERSONAL

ACTION STEPS

SPIRITUAL

ACTION STEPS

CAREER

ACTION STEPS

TOOLS AND TASKS FOR FEBRUARY

Explore the healing power of yantras, herbs/spices, oils, yoga postures, and habits. Feel the effects on the body, mind, and spirit. Write down how they connect to your divine life.

HERB/SPICE
Fennel

HABIT
Self-Love
abhyanga oil
massage

OIL
Rose

YOGA POSE
Boat Pose
Navasana

WRITE YOUR ACCOMPLISHMENTS FOR THE MONTH

VICTORIES

....

....

....

....

....

....

ENLIGHTENED EXPERIENCE

....

....

....

....

....

....

REWARD

....

....

....

....

....

....

WHAT DID NOT HAPPEN AND WHY?

....

....

....

....

....

....

MONTHLY REVIEW

DID I ACCOMPLISH ALL MY GOALS FOR THE MONTH?

MY TOP 3 ACCOMPLISHMENTS FOR THE MONTH

MY TOP 3 CHALLENGES FOR THE MONTH

WERE MY ACTIONS IN ALIGNMENT WITH WHO I ASPIRE TO BE?

I AM THANKFUL FOR

WHAT MAKES ME HAPPY?

“

The body is your temple.
Keep it pure and clean for the soul to reside in.

– B.K.S. IYENGAR

BLESSINGS AND GRATITUDE

AFFIRMATIONS

MARCH

SHIVA

(God of Destruction and Rebirth)

Lord Shiva is known as Mahadev, or Great God. He is one of the three Gods of Trimurti (Hindu Trinity). His title is the Destroyer, or Transformer. Believed to be Aadi (without a beginning) and Ananth (limitless), he is unchanging and formless. His name refers to someone who is eternally pure and cannot be contaminated.

God Shiva is considered to be the epitome of compassion among the gods. He lives on Mount Kailash with his wife, Goddess Parvati, and their three children, Ganesha, Ashok-Sundari, and Kartikeya.

The scriptures describe him as fair, like an ice mountain, wearing animal hide for clothes. His throat is blue, as he once drank the deadliest poison to protect the entire Universe. Lord Shiva has a third eye on his forehead. He wears a snake around his neck called Vasuki. A garland of skulls and bells are his ornaments and he bears the crescent moon on his head.

The holy river Ganges flows from his matted hair. He rides a bull called Nandi, with his trident in one hand and the Damaru, or hourglass-shaped drum, in the other. Lord Shiva sits on a tiger skin alongside his wife Goddess Parvati, surrounded by his ganas, or attendants.

Lord Shiva is regarded as the patron God of Yoga and Arts. He destroys the demon of ignorance. By worshiping Shiva, you will be guided in destroying negative energy in your life.

MANTRA

SOUND

Om Namah Shivaya!

MEANING

Om, Adoration to Lord Shiva.

BIJA MANTRA: *HROUM*

MARCH

MON	TUE	WED	THU	FRI	SAT	SUN

MY GOALS

PERSONAL

ACTION STEPS

SPIRITUAL

ACTION STEPS

CAREER

ACTION STEPS

TOOLS AND TASKS FOR MARCH

Explore the healing power of yantras, herbs/spices, oils, yoga postures, and habits. Feel the effects on the body, mind, and spirit. Write down how they connect to your divine life.

HERB/SPICE
Saffron

HABIT
Energy movement

OIL
Frankincense

YOGA POSE
Chair Pose
Utkatasana

WRITE YOUR ACCOMPLISHMENTS FOR THE MONTH

VICTORIES

....

....

....

....

....

....

ENLIGHTENED EXPERIENCE

....

....

....

....

....

....

REWARD

....

....

....

....

....

....

WHAT DID NOT HAPPEN AND WHY?

....

....

....

....

....

....

MONTHLY REVIEW

DID I ACCOMPLISH ALL MY GOALS FOR THE MONTH?

MY TOP 3 ACCOMPLISHMENTS FOR THE MONTH

MY TOP 3 CHALLENGES FOR THE MONTH

WERE MY ACTIONS IN ALIGNMENT WITH WHO I ASPIRE TO BE?

I AM THANKFUL FOR

WHAT MAKES ME HAPPY?

“

Knowledge of constitution is the key for a holistic and integral health care, the true basis of any preventative medicine.

– VASANT LAD

BLESSINGS AND GRATITUDE

AFFIRMATIONS

APRIL

SITA

(Goddess of Femininity and Fertility)

Goddess Sita is known as the Goddess of Femininity and Fertility. She was born from the deep earth when Lord Janaka was ploughing in the field. "Janaki" is one of her names because she was considered the adoptive daughter of Lord Janaka. The goddess is known for her self-sacrifice, courage, and purity.

She descended as the daughter of Mother Earth and a symbol of fertility, abundance, and well-being. Lord Rama had descended as Maryada Purushottam (most virtuous man), and Sita complemented Lord Rama as an epitome of feminine virtue. She has been described as a woman of serene beauty, exemplary virtue, and an ideal daughter, wife, and mother.

Goddess Sita wears a golden crown filled with emeralds, pearls, and rubies. Her hair is tucked under her blue-and-pink sari adorned with golden emeralds. Her body is a symbol of her divine royalty and is decorated with a matching belt, jeweled bangles, and necklaces. Her skin is soft and brown like the earth. She sits on a royal throne next to her beloved Rama. Animals and flowers are always surrounding her.

The values of womanly virtue and grace represented by Goddess Sita are still held sacred today. You can call on her to show you genuine love and compassion for others.

MANTRA

SOUND

"Sita Ram, Sita Ram, Sita Ram, Jaya Sita Ram."

MEANING

Sita symbolizes the perfect woman while Ram signifies strength. "Jaya" means victory.

BIJA MANTRA: *RAM*

APRIL

MON	TUE	WED	THU	FRI	SAT	SUN

MY GOALS

PERSONAL

ACTION STEPS

SPIRITUAL

ACTION STEPS

CAREER

ACTION STEPS

TOOLS AND TASKS FOR APRIL

Explore the healing power of yantras, herbs/spices, oils, yoga postures, and habits. Feel the effects on the body, mind, and spirit. Write down how they connect to your divine life.

HERB/SPICE
Mint

HABIT
Space cleanse/purge

OIL
Helichrysum

YOGA POSE
Seated Twist Marichyasana

WRITE YOUR ACCOMPLISHMENTS FOR THE MONTH

VICTORIES

....

....

....

....

....

....

ENLIGHTENED EXPERIENCE

....

....

....

....

....

....

REWARD

....

....

....

....

....

....

WHAT DID NOT HAPPEN AND WHY?

....

....

....

....

....

....

MONTHLY REVIEW

DID I ACCOMPLISH ALL MY GOALS FOR THE MONTH?

MY TOP 3 ACCOMPLISHMENTS FOR THE MONTH

MY TOP 3 CHALLENGES FOR THE MONTH

WERE MY ACTIONS IN ALIGNMENT WITH WHO I ASPIRE TO BE?

I AM THANKFUL FOR

WHAT MAKES ME HAPPY?

“

Even death is not to be feared by one who has lived wisely.

– BUDDHA

BLESSINGS AND GRATITUDE

AFFIRMATIONS

MAY

YASHODA

(Unconditional Parental Love)

Ma Yashoda, also popularly called Yashoda Maiyya, was the foster-mother of Lord Krishna. She was the wife of Nanda Raja, the King of Brij, the cow-herding community who lived near the banks of the river Yamuna.

One day, Yashoda woke up and found an amazingly beautiful child by her side; she wept with joy. Being already in her middle age, she had waited long to have a child, so her exhilaration was immense upon witnessing the birth of her son, Krishna.

Yashoda was a dedicated mother to Krishna, and this can be seen in the leelas (pastimes) of his childhood. The leelas show the Supreme God acting like a child in front of a human being. The Lord, with all his powers, had shaken with fear upon seeing a small stick in the hands of Yashoda. Such was the love of Yashoda that made the Lord of the Universe forget his powers and love her unconditionally. Hence, Yashoda is always depicted with the young Lord Krishna.

A fascinating story that showed the contrast and affinity of the divine and the mortal was when Yashoda made Krishna open his mouth after learning that the child was eating mud. He refused. She was almost ready to beat him with a stick, but Krishna was afraid and finally gave in. To Yashoda's bewilderment, she saw the Vishwaroop, or entire Universe, inside his mouth.

Ma Yashoda is the epitome of unconditional love. Call on her for help with loving your children or family members.

MANTRA

SOUND
"Yashoda ka Krishna Kanaiya?"

MEANING
What will Yashoda do with mischievous Krishna?

BIJA MANTRA: *HRIM*

MAY

MON	TUE	WED	THU	FRI	SAT	SUN

MY GOALS

PERSONAL

ACTION STEPS

SPIRITUAL

ACTION STEPS

CAREER

ACTION STEPS

TOOLS AND TASKS FOR MAY

Explore the healing power of yantras, herbs/spices, oils, yoga postures, and habits. Feel the effects on the body, mind, and spirit. Write down how they connect to your divine life.

HERB/SPICE
Cilantro

HABIT
Life-Style
earlier &
lighter dinner

OIL
Tea Tree

YOGA POSE
Bridge Pose
Setu Bandha
Sarvangasana

WRITE YOUR ACCOMPLISHMENTS FOR THE MONTH

VICTORIES

ENLIGHTENED EXPERIENCE

REWARD

WHAT DID NOT HAPPEN AND WHY?

MONTHLY REVIEW

DID I ACCOMPLISH ALL MY GOALS FOR THE MONTH?

MY TOP 3 ACCOMPLISHMENTS FOR THE MONTH

MY TOP 3 CHALLENGES FOR THE MONTH

WERE MY ACTIONS IN ALIGNMENT WITH WHO I ASPIRE TO BE?

I AM THANKFUL FOR

WHAT MAKES ME HAPPY?

> *The voice of inner truth says, 'I embrace the unknown because it allows me to see new aspects of myself'*
>
> – DEEPAK CHOPRA

BLESSINGS AND GRATITUDE

AFFIRMATIONS

JUNE

GANESHA

(God of New Beginnings)

Lord Ganesha is the God of New Beginnings and Remover of Obstacles. A very important deity in Hinduism, he is bestowed with the title of Pratham Pujya, or *First to be Worshiped.* His consorts are Buddhi (Intellect) and Riddhi/Siddhi (Prosperity and Spiritual Power).

Lord Ganesha is the son of Lord Shiva and Goddess Parvati. As a boy, Lord Shiva beheaded him because he hindered his departure. His grieving mother, Goddess Parvati, decided to end the Universe with her rage when she found out about the fate of her son. All the gods, including Shiva, promised to bring Ganesha back to life. Lord Shiva sent his ganas to look for a head for his son. They found Gajaraj, a pious elephant who had prayed for ages to attain Moksha (liberation), and who happily offered his head.

Lord Ganesha has an elephant head with a curved trunk and huge fan ears. He has a hefty body with a pot belly. Often, he is depicted either with four or six arms. His arms hold a Shanka (conch shell), a Farsa (axe), a Mala (rosary), a lotus flower, and a Laddu or Modak (sweets), and one of his right hands is Abhaya Mudra (blessing his devotees). One of his tusks is broken, which he used to write the Vedas. His vehicle is a rat, or Mushka.

He is a patron God of all Indians, irrespective of caste, creed, region, or religion.

MANTRA

SOUND

"Vakra-Tunndda Maha-Kaaya Suurya-Kotti Samaprabha Nirvighnam Kuru Me Deva Sarva-Kaaryessu Sarvadaa."

MEANING

O Lord Ganesha, of curved trunk, large body, and the brilliance of a million suns, please remove all obstacles from all my deeds.

BIJA MANTRA: GAM

JUNE

MON	TUE	WED	THU	FRI	SAT	SUN

MY GOALS

PERSONAL

ACTION STEPS

SPIRITUAL

ACTION STEPS

CAREER

ACTION STEPS

TOOLS AND TASKS FOR JUNE

Explore the healing power of yantras, herbs/spices, oils, yoga postures, and habits. Feel the effects on the body, mind, and spirit. Write down how they connect to your divine life.

HERB/SPICE
Aloe Vera

HABIT
Surrender sleep/bed by 10 p.m.

OIL
Lavender

YOGA POSE
Cobra
Bhujangasana

WRITE YOUR ACCOMPLISHMENTS FOR THE MONTH

VICTORIES

ENLIGHTENED EXPERIENCE

REWARD

WHAT DID NOT HAPPEN AND WHY?

MONTHLY REVIEW

DID I ACCOMPLISH ALL MY GOALS FOR THE MONTH?

MY TOP 3 ACCOMPLISHMENTS FOR THE MONTH

MY TOP 3 CHALLENGES FOR THE MONTH

WERE MY ACTIONS IN ALIGNMENT WITH WHO I ASPIRE TO BE?

I AM THANKFUL FOR

WHAT MAKES ME HAPPY?

“

The nature of the mind is to jump all over the place, and it does, that’s why meditation is so important.

– MAYA TIWARI

BLESSINGS AND GRATITUDE

AFFIRMATIONS

JULY

SARASWATI

(Goddess of Knowledge, Music, and Art)

Goddess Saraswati is the divine wife of Lord Brahma. She is one of the Tridevi (Three Goddesses), the other two being Lakshmi and Parvati, the divine partners of the Trimurti (Hindu Trinity), Brahma, Vishnu, and Shiva. She has many names, including Sharada, Veenapani, and Vagdevi.

She is the Goddess of Knowledge, Music, and Art and is worshiped widely across India equally by Hindus, Jains, and Buddhists. Before beginning their education, children are encouraged to seek her divine grace. In India, musical instruments and books are respected and considered her manifestations.

Goddess Saraswati is described to have very distinct attire. She wears a pure white sari and rides a white swan. She is extremely fair and beautiful and has four arms holding the Veena (a musical instrument), a Mala (rosary), a Kamandalu (water pot), and a manuscript. She has her foot on a white Lotus and her pet Mayura (peacock) sitting next to her.

Triveni Sangam in Prayag (Allahabad), India is the meeting point of the three most sacred rivers of India: Ganga, Yamuna, and Saraswati. It is said that she once incarnated on Earth as River Saraswati, which slowly disappeared and now flows invisibly.

Knowledge is useful both for the material as well as the spiritual life, which takes us toward our goal. You can worship Goddess Saraswati to help you with acquiring new knowledge in your studies or career.

MANTRA

SOUND

"Om Aim Maha Sarasvatyai Namah."

MEANING

O Goddess Saraswati, salutations to you. O giver of boons and fulfiller of desires. I am going to start my studies. With your blessings may there be success always.

BIJA MANTRA: *AYEIM*

JULY

MON	TUE	WED	THU	FRI	SAT	SUN

MY GOALS

PERSONAL

ACTION STEPS

SPIRITUAL

ACTION STEPS

CAREER

ACTION STEPS

TOOLS AND TASKS FOR JULY

Explore the healing power of yantras, herbs/spices, oils, yoga postures, and habits. Feel the effects on the body, mind, and spirit. Write down how they connect to your divine life.

HERB/SPICE
Cumin

HABIT
Connection
wake up early

OIL
Lemon

YOGA POSE
Side Plank,
Vashithasana

WRITE YOUR ACCOMPLISHMENTS FOR THE MONTH

MONTHLY REVIEW

DID I ACCOMPLISH ALL MY GOALS FOR THE MONTH?

MY TOP 3 ACCOMPLISHMENTS FOR THE MONTH

MY TOP 3 CHALLENGES FOR THE MONTH

WERE MY ACTIONS IN ALIGNMENT WITH WHO I ASPIRE TO BE?

I AM THANKFUL FOR

WHAT MAKES ME HAPPY?

"

Put your heart, mind, and soul into even your smallest acts. This is the secret of success.

– SIVANANDA

BLESSINGS AND GRATITUDE

AFFIRMATIONS

AUGUST

GANGA

(River Goddess)

Goddess Ganga, popularly known as the Holy River Ganges, has been a very important part of the Hindu religion in every aspect. She washes away sins and helps find moksha, or liberation. Her water is considered the sanctum of purity; no religious ceremony or custom can be complete without it.

Ancient scriptures state that during one of Lord Vishnu's incarnations, the sweat from his feet fell into Lord Brahma's Kamandalu (water-pot) and Ganga was born. At the request of the gods, she flowed across the heavens to facilitate and purify their rituals.

She is mostly depicted as a fair and beautiful Goddess with four arms. One hand holds a Kalasha (water pot), another a lotus, and her other two hands are shown as giving blessings and receiving sins from the devotees. She wears pure white clothes and rides a crocodile.

Ganga stayed in the heavens until a sage cursed her so that she will need to fall on Earth and keep cleansing the sins of mankind until the end of time. Meanwhile, King Bhagiratha prayed to Lord Brahma to release the holy waters of Ganga to save the entire Earth from draught. With Lord Shiva's help, Ganga was released and flowed down to Earth.

Goddess Ganga has been the symbol of purity and the backbone of all Hindu ceremonies since time immemorial.

MANTRA

SOUND

"Devi Sureshvari Bhagavati Gange Tribhuvana-Taarinni Tarala-Tarangge Shankara-Mauli-Vihaarinni Vimale Mama Matir-Aastaam Tava Pada-Kamale."

MEANING

O Goddess of the Gods of Heaven, Mother Ganga, who flows through all three worlds, and liberates them with your liquid waves. You are the purest of all and meander on Shankara's crown. May my whole devotion be fixed at your lotus feet.

BIJA MANTRA: GANG

AUGUST

MON	TUE	WED	THU	FRI	SAT	SUN

MY GOALS

PERSONAL

ACTION STEPS

SPIRITUAL

ACTION STEPS

CAREER

ACTION STEPS

TOOLS AND TASKS FOR AUGUST

Explore the healing power of yantras, herbs/spices, oils, yoga postures, and habits. Feel the effects on the body, mind, and spirit. Write down how they connect to your divine life.

HERB/SPICE
Turmeric

HABIT
Digestion
tongue
scraping

OIL
Camomile

YOGA POSE
Child's Pose
Balasana

WRITE YOUR ACCOMPLISHMENTS FOR THE MONTH

VICTORIES

....

....

....

....

....

....

ENLIGHTENED EXPERIENCE

....

....

....

....

....

....

REWARD

....

....

....

....

....

....

WHAT DID NOT HAPPEN AND WHY?

....

....

....

....

....

....

MONTHLY REVIEW

DID I ACCOMPLISH ALL
MY GOALS FOR THE MONTH?

MY TOP 3 ACCOMPLISHMENTS
FOR THE MONTH

MY TOP 3 CHALLENGES
FOR THE MONTH

WERE MY ACTIONS IN ALIGNMENT
WITH WHO I ASPIRE TO BE?

I AM THANKFUL FOR

WHAT MAKES ME HAPPY?

“

Since everything is a reflection of our minds, everything can be changed by our minds.

– BUDDHA

BLESSINGS AND GRATITUDE

AFFIRMATIONS

SEPTEMBER

DHANWANTARI
(Physician of the Gods)

Lord Dhanwantari is one of the many avatars (incarnations) of Lord Vishnu. He is also considered the patron God of Ayurveda and the Physician of the Gods.

Along with many other mystical objects and beings, God Dhanwantari emerged out of the Kshir Sagara carrying Amruta Kalasha, or a pot of Elixir/Ambrosia. There is another legend which states that God Dhanwantari was the King of Varanasi, a city in Northern India where he practiced ancient medical science. His disciple, Sishruta, later wrote the Sishruta Samhita, a manuscript on the medical science of surgery.

Being an incarnation of Lord Vishnu, he is often depicted as a four-armed attractive god rising out of the ocean. Two of his arms hold the Shankha (conch shell) and Sri Chakra (disc-shaped weapon) of Lord Vishnu. The Amruta Kalasha is held by the third hand and Jalauka (a leech) by the fourth one. Sometimes, he is also shown as holding herbs, or the scriptures of Ayurveda.

Ayurveda practitioners around the world revere God Dhanwantari, and his pictures or idols can usually be seen in their premises. Dhanteras is considered to be the day God Dhanwantari appeared; hence on this day Hindus across India offer prayers and seek blessings from him for good health and long life.

MANTRA

SOUND

"Om Namo Bhagavate Mah Sudharshana Vasudevaaya Dhanvantaraye; Amrutha Kalasa Hasthaaya Sarva Bhaya Vinaasaaya Sarva Roka Nivaaranaaya Thri Lokya Pathaye Thri Lokya Nithaye Sri Maha Vishnu Swarupa Sri Dhanvantri Swarupa Sri Sri Sri Aoushata Chakra Narayana Swaha."

MEANING

Our salutations to the Lord who is known as Sudarshana Vasudeva Dhanvantari, who holds the Kalasha full of nectar of immortality and removes all fears by removing all diseases. Dhanvantari is Lord Vishnu himself empowered to heal the Jivatmas. We bow to the sumpreme Lord of Ayurveda.

BIJA MANTRA: *SHREE*

SEPTEMBER

MON	TUE	WED	THU	FRI	SAT	SUN

MY GOALS

PERSONAL

ACTION STEPS

SPIRITUAL

ACTION STEPS

CAREER

ACTION STEPS

TOOLS AND TASKS FOR SEPTEMBER

Explore the healing power of yantras, herbs/spices, oils, yoga postures, and habits. Feel the effects on the body, mind, and spirit. Write down how they connect to your divine life.

HERB/SPICE
Cardamom

HABIT
Achievement
forgiveness
gratitude

OIL
Neem

YOGA POSE
Legs up the wall
Viparita Karani

WRITE YOUR ACCOMPLISHMENTS FOR THE MONTH

VICTORIES

ENLIGHTENED EXPERIENCE

REWARD

WHAT DID NOT HAPPEN AND WHY?

MONTHLY REVIEW

DID I ACCOMPLISH ALL MY GOALS FOR THE MONTH?

MY TOP 3 ACCOMPLISHMENTS FOR THE MONTH

MY TOP 3 CHALLENGES FOR THE MONTH

WERE MY ACTIONS IN ALIGNMENT WITH WHO I ASPIRE TO BE?

I AM THANKFUL FOR

WHAT MAKES ME HAPPY?

Meet everybody and every circumstance on the battlefield of life with the courage of a hero and the smile of a conqueror.

– PARAMAHANSA YOGANANDA

BLESSINGS AND GRATITUDE

AFFIRMATIONS

OCTOBER

DURGA

(The Mother Goddess)

Goddess Durga is the incarnation of Goddess Parvati, Lord Shiva's wife. Her incarnation was necessitated to annihilate a very powerful demon called Mahishasura (Buffalo Demon), who had overpowered all the Gods of heaven. Only a combined Shakti (energy) of the Trimurti (Hindu Trinity)—namely Lord Shiva, Lord Vishnu, and Lord Brahma—could defeat him. They combined their powers and gave form to Goddess Durga.

All the other Gods also gave their weapons to her. Even with all the weapons in her hand, she looks very beautiful. Even while killing the demon, there is no sign of anger, only peace and a smile on her face. She slayed the evil and mighty Buffalo Demon. Frequently, she is shown holding the head of Mahishasura in one of her hands, and her lion is shown killing a buffalo.

Goddess Durga wears a beautiful red sari and a gold crown, a garland of fresh flowers and exquisite ornaments. She is mostly depicted riding a lion, has ten hands, and all the hands have the best weapons from different Gods, including Indira's thunderbolt, Vishnu's Sudarshana Chakra, Lord Shiva's Trishul (trident), and many other weapons. On her forehead there is a third eye similar to Lord Shiva's.

Goddess Durga is considered the mother of all creation and protector of good from evil. Reach out to her for guidance in battling the evil in your heart.

MANTRA

SOUND

"Sarva Mangal Maangalye Shivey
Sarvarth Saadhike Sharanye
Trayambake Gauri Narayani
Namostutey."

Meaning

O noble wife of Lord Shiva, one who fulfills all our purposes with auspiciousness. I have come to your refuge, O three-eyed Gauri, Narayani, I pray to you.

BIJA MANTRA: *DOOM*

OCTOBER

MON	TUE	WED	THU	FRI	SAT	SUN

MY GOALS

PERSONAL

ACTION STEPS

SPIRITUAL

ACTION STEPS

CAREER

ACTION STEPS

TOOLS AND TASKS FOR OCTOBER

Explore the healing power of yantras, herbs/spices, oils, yoga postures, and habits. Feel the effects on the body, mind, and spirit. Write down how they connect to your divine life.

HERB/SPICE
Cinnamon

HABIT
Intelligence connect to nature

OIL
Eucalyptus

YOGA POSE
Supported Shoulder Stand Sarvangasana

WRITE YOUR ACCOMPLISHMENTS FOR THE MONTH

VICTORIES

ENLIGHTENED EXPERIENCE

REWARD

WHAT DID NOT HAPPEN AND WHY?

MONTHLY REVIEW

DID I ACCOMPLISH ALL
MY GOALS FOR THE MONTH?

MY TOP 3 ACCOMPLISHMENTS
FOR THE MONTH

MY TOP 3 CHALLENGES
FOR THE MONTH

WERE MY ACTIONS IN ALIGNMENT
WITH WHO I ASPIRE TO BE?

I AM THANKFUL FOR

WHAT MAKES ME HAPPY?

“

Love beautifies the giver and elevates the receiver.

– SIVANANDA

BLESSINGS AND GRATITUDE

AFFIRMATIONS

NOVEMBER

LAKSHMI

(Goddess of Wealth, Prosperity, and Good Fortune)

Goddess Lakshmi is the Goddess of Wealth, Prosperity, and Good Fortune. She is the wife of Lord Vishnu and they live in the Kshir Sagara (Ocean of Milk). She is also called Shree, Shreedevi, Vaishnavi, and Vishnupriya, among others.

According to the Puranas (Hindu scriptures), the Devtas (Gods) and the Asuras (Demons) were churning the Kshir Sagara to bring out its bounties. Goddess Lakshmi emerged out of the ocean and everyone was mesmerized by her beauty. She was given the option to choose her groom. Captivated by his youth, vitality, and radiance, she chose Vishnu as her husband and put a garland around his neck.

Goddess Lakshmi is usually depicted as extremely beautiful, wearing a red sari lined with gold. Her entire body is heavily decorated with exquisite gold ornaments. She is either standing or sitting on a lotus flower. She has four hands; one is shown showering gold coins, one has a Kalasha (pot) topped with a coconut, and the other two hands are either described holding a lotus flower or in a mudra (gesture) of blessing. There are two white elephants behind her holding flowers, a garland, or Kalasha in their trunks. Sometimes a white owl called Peechaka is shown sitting by her side; this owl is considered her vehicle.

Goddess Lakshmi is invoked by offering prayer during Diwali, or the Festival of Lights. You can call on her for prosperity and abundance.

MANTRA

SOUND

"Om Shreem Maha Lakshmaiye Namaha."

MEANING

O great Goddess Lakshmi, salutations to you.

BIJA MANTRA: *SHREEM*

NOVEMBER

MON	TUE	WED	THU	FRI	SAT	SUN

MY GOALS

PERSONAL

ACTION STEPS

SPIRITUAL

ACTION STEPS

CAREER

ACTION STEPS

TOOLS AND TASKS FOR NOVEMBER

Explore the healing power of yantras, herbs/spices, oils, yoga postures, and habits. Feel the effects on the body, mind, and spirit. Write down how they connect to your divine life.

HERB/SPICE
Ginger

HABIT
Sensory Impressions sense organ care

OIL
Rosemary

YOGA POSE
Seated Head to Knee Pose
Janu Sirasana

WRITE YOUR ACCOMPLISHMENTS FOR THE MONTH

VICTORIES

ENLIGHTENED EXPERIENCE

REWARD

WHAT DID NOT HAPPEN AND WHY?

MONTHLY REVIEW

DID I ACCOMPLISH ALL
MY GOALS FOR THE MONTH?

MY TOP 3 ACCOMPLISHMENTS
FOR THE MONTH

MY TOP 3 CHALLENGES
FOR THE MONTH

WERE MY ACTIONS IN ALIGNMENT
WITH WHO I ASPIRE TO BE?

I AM THANKFUL FOR

WHAT MAKES ME HAPPY?

"

If you don't like something, change it. If you can't change it, change your attitude. Don't complain.

– MAYA ANGELOU

BLESSINGS AND GRATITUDE

AFFIRMATIONS

DECEMBER

KALI

(Goddess of Death and Time)

Goddess Kali is known as the Goddess of Death and Time. Her presence signifies time which gives her the power to devour everything. Kali has an ethereal beauty, captivating for both Gods and humans. She embodies empowerment, or Shakti—the female energy, creativity, and fertility. Her consort is Lord Shiva.

Ma Kali wears a garland of skulls and a skirt of dismembered arms. They depict her compassion for her children by having liberated them from their attachment to the limitations of their bodies. She holds a sword freshly dripping in blood. Her skin is dark blue or black. She is a courageous Goddess, a destroyer of evil and killer of demons.

Mother Kali stands or dances on Shiva who is beneath her; the contrast of her black skin and Shiva's white skin is evident. But Shiva's expression is one of calmness. Sometimes the Goddess is shown with four arms, while at other times she becomes a ten-armed Mahakali form. She has disheveled hair, small fangs, and her tongue is usually out.

In her four-armed position, she is riding a lion and holding a sword and lotuses. Her unique and terrible form makes her a great protector. Despite her physical appearance, she is considered the kindest and most compassionate of all the Goddesses. Often, she is regarded by her devotees as the mother of the entire Universe.

You can call on her to battle the demons that disturb your mind, heart, and spirit.

MANTRA

SOUND
"Om Krim Kalikayai Namah."

MEANING
I bow my head to the Goddess Kali.

BIJA MANTRA: *KREEM*

DECEMBER

MON	TUE	WED	THU	FRI	SAT	SUN

MY GOALS

PERSONAL

ACTION STEPS

SPIRITUAL

ACTION STEPS

CAREER

ACTION STEPS

TOOLS AND TASKS FOR DECEMBER

Explore the healing power of yantras, herbs/spices, oils, yoga postures, and habits. Feel the effects on the body, mind, and spirit. Write down how they connect to your divine life.

HERB/SPICE
Rosemary

HABIT
Contentment
laughter/joy!

OIL
Sandalwood

YOGA POSE
Lion Pose
Simhasana

WRITE YOUR ACCOMPLISHMENTS FOR THE MONTH

VICTORIES

....

....

....

....

....

....

ENLIGHTENED EXPERIENCE

....

....

....

....

....

....

REWARD

....

....

....

....

....

....

WHAT DID NOT HAPPEN AND WHY?

....

....

....

....

....

....

MONTHLY REVIEW

DID I ACCOMPLISH ALL
MY GOALS FOR THE MONTH?

MY TOP 3 ACCOMPLISHMENTS
FOR THE MONTH

MY TOP 3 CHALLENGES
FOR THE MONTH

WERE MY ACTIONS IN ALIGNMENT
WITH WHO I ASPIRE TO BE?

I AM THANKFUL FOR

WHAT MAKES ME HAPPY?

"

I am not afraid of storms for I am learning how to sail my ship.

– LOUISA MAY ALCOTT

BLESSINGS AND GRATITUDE

AFFIRMATIONS

AYURVEDA
YOGA LIFESTYLE HABITS

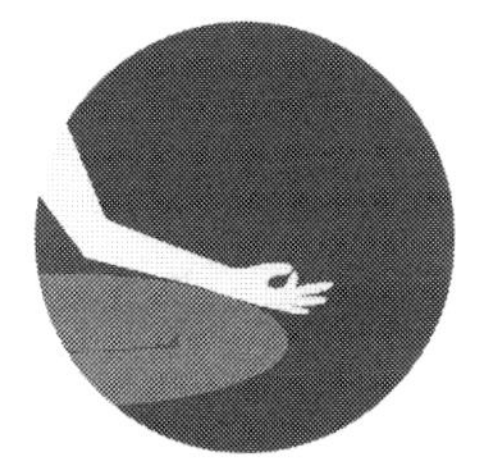

Mindfulness
meditation/pranayama

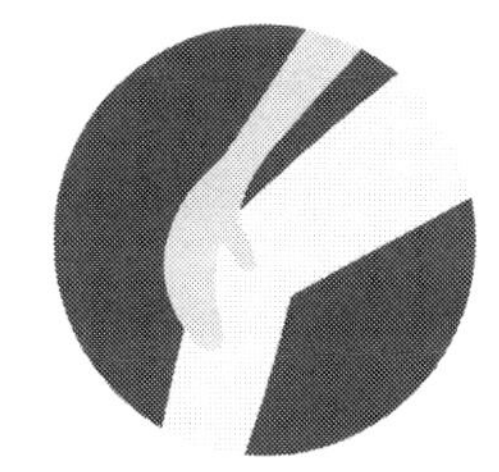

Self-Love
abhyanga/oil massage

Energy
movement

Space
cleanse/purge

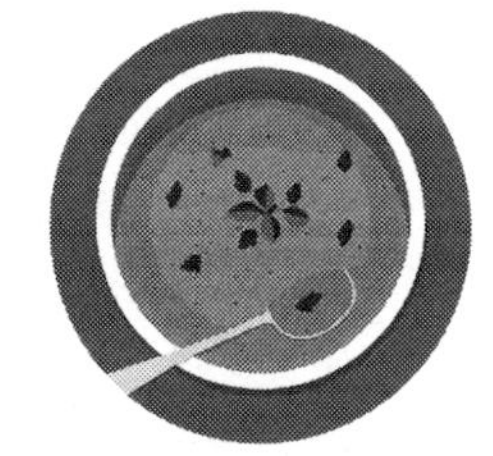

Lifestyle
earlier & lighter dinner

Surrender
sleep/bed by 10 p.m.

Connection
wake up early

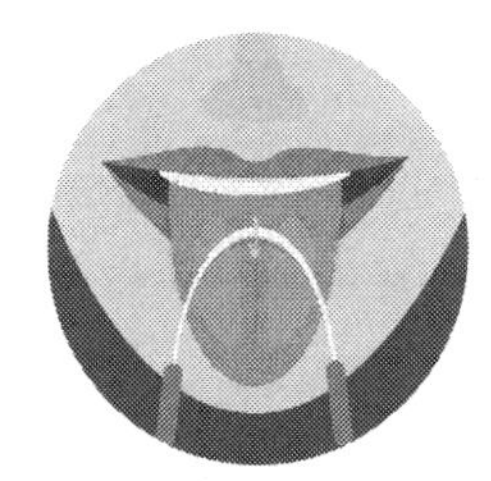

Digestion
tongue scraping

Achievement
forgiveness/gratitude

Intelligence
connect to nature

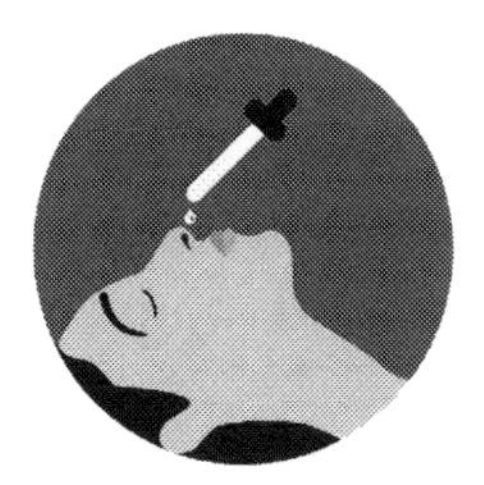

Sensory Therapy
sense organ care

Contentment
laughter/Joy!

THE THREE DOSHAS

Biological energies found throughout the human body and mind.

 VATA AIR + ETHER	 PITTA FIRE + WATER	 KAPHA EARTH + WATER
Energy of action, transportation and movement	Energy of transformation, conversion and metabolism	Energy of construction, lubrication, nourishment
Light, dry, cold, rough, subtle, mobile	Hot, sharp, oily, liquid, acidic	Heavy, cold, moist, dull, soft, sticky, static
SEASON Fall/Early Winter	SEASON Late Spring/Summer	SEASON Late Winter/Early Spring
BODY Long, lean	BODY Well-defined, good muscles	BODY Large, well-developed, stocky
LOCATION Colon, bones, joints, ears, brain, nerve tissues	LOCATION Small intestine digestion, liver, spleen, pancreas, blood, eyes, skin	LOCATION Stomach, chest, lungs, throat, head, lymph, fatty tissue, reproductive tissue
IMBALANCED BODY Constipation, dry skin, dry hair, arthritis, anemic, poor circulation	IMBALANCED BODY Migranes, headaches, heartburn, skin rashes, hypertension	IMBALANCED BODY Obesity, mucus, congestion
BALANCED MIND Energetic, creative, good communication, adaptable, positive	BALANCED MIND Enlightened, intelligent, courageous, friendly	BALANCED MIND Loving, patient, compassionate, stable, loyal
IMBALANCED MIND Fearful, anxious, indecisive, unreliable, hyperactive	IMBALANCED MIND Angry, aggressive, manipulating, egotistic	IMBALANCED MIND Insecure, lethargic, controlling

AYURVEDA DOSHA QUIZ

	Vata (Air)	Pitta (Fire)	Kapha (Water)
Frame	☐ thin, lanky	☐ medium, balanced	☐ large, well developed
Height	☐ tall or short	☐ medium	☐ short or tall
Weight	☐ light	☐ moderate	☐ heavy
Skin	☐ dry, rough	☐ red, sensitive, lusterous	☐ plum, full of moisture
Eyes	☐ small	☐ piercing, inflamed	☐ large, white
Hair	☐ thin, dry	☐ oily, soft	☐ thick, wavy
Teeth	☐ crooked	☐ moderate	☐ large
Lips	☐ thin, small	☐ medium, red	☐ full, large
Nails	☐ brittle	☐ bendable	☐ strong
Sweat	☐ scantly	☐ profuse	☐ moderate
Stool	☐ hard, dry	☐ loose,soft	☐ normal
Urine	☐ scanty	☐ profuse, yellow	☐ moderate, clear
Sensitivity	☐ cold	☐ hot	☐ damp
Immune Function	☐ low	☐ moderate	☐ high
Activity	☐ restless	☐ active	☐ slow
Endurance	☐ exhausted	☐ moderate	☐ high
Sleep	☐ poor	☐ variable	☐ excess
Dreams	☐ restless, flying	☐ colorful, conflicts	☐ romantic, water
Memory	☐ absent-minded	☐ sharp	☐ slow
Speech	☐ fast, forgetful	☐ sharp, fluid	☐ slow, reserved
Temperament	☐ nervous	☐ motivated	☐ conservative
Emotions	☐ fear	☐ anger	☐ attachment
Faith	☐ erratic	☐ strong	☐ steady
Relationships	☐ unreliable	☐ domineering	☐ clinging
Routine	☐ unsustained	☐ determined	☐ slow
	Vata	Pitta	Kapha
Total			

AYURVEDIC CLOCK

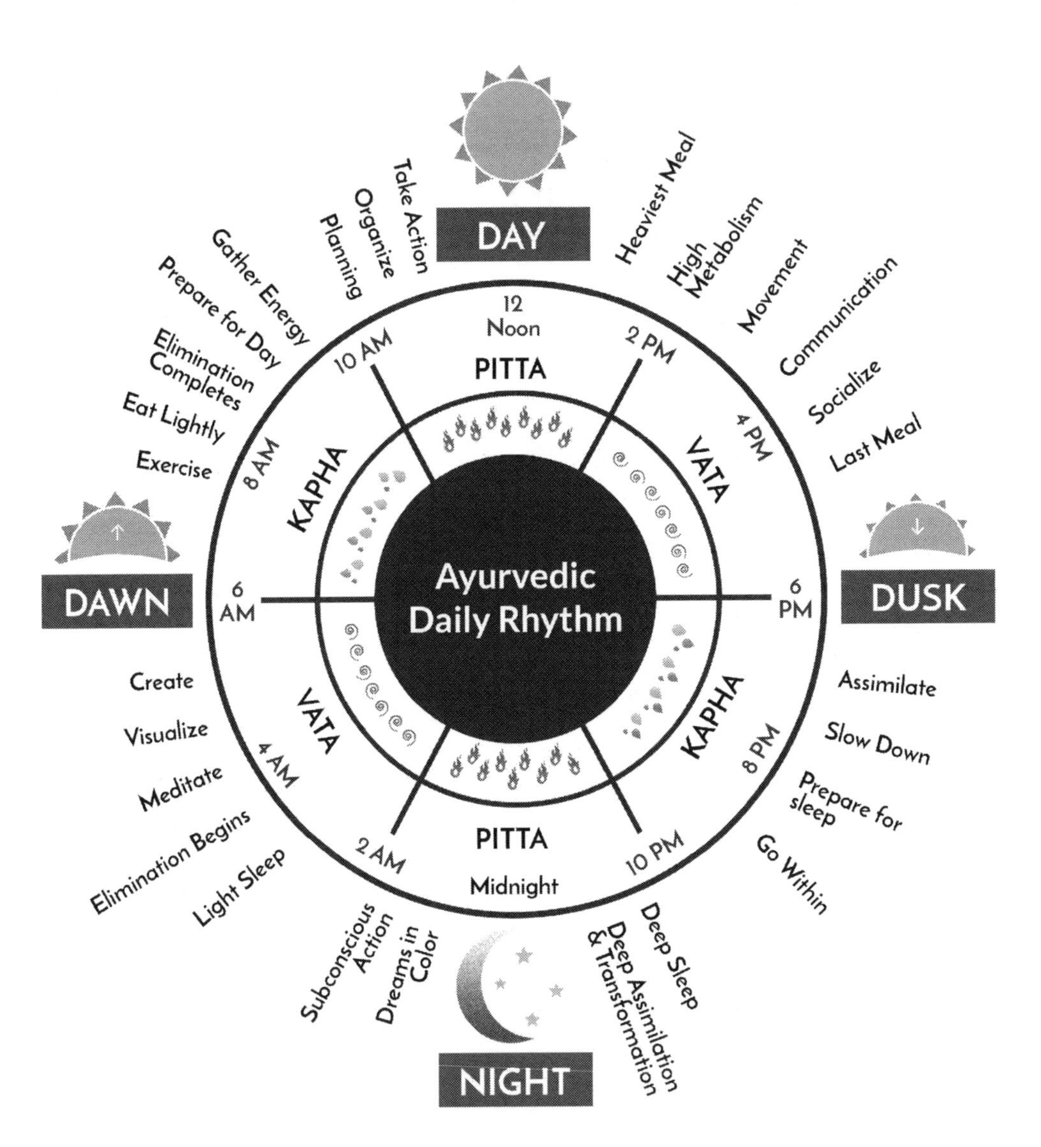

Align your daily rhythms in tune with Nature's rhythms. Support your day by the dominant energy inside and around you. Each day we cycle through the three doshas: Vata, Pitta, Kapha. The day is divided into six four-hour cycles. To live a life from turbulance to calm we must follow the Ayurvedic Clock.

AYURVEDA CHECKLIST

Date: ________ Time: ________ Ayurvedic Pulse: V P K

Quality of Arising:

Happy ☐ Energetic ☐ Restless ☐ Tired ☐
Stiff ☐ Pain ☐ Difficulty getting up ☐ Excited to start the day ☐

Others: ________

Morning Activities:

Meditation ☐ Yoga ☐ Pranayama ☐ Breath Body Movement ☐
Outdoor ☐ Walk/Jog ☐ Stretching ☐ Pooping ☐
Exercise ☐ Listening to Radio ☐ Watching TV ☐ Computer ☐
Work ☐ School ☐ Cleaning ☐ Cooking ☐
Shopping ☐ Errands ☐

Other: ________

Sense Organ Care:

Tongue Scraping ☐ Oil Pulling ☐ Oiling Nostrils/Nasya ☐ Dry Skin Brushing ☐
Oiling Body/Abhyanga ☐ Brushing/Oiling Hair ☐ Eye Exercise ☐ Bathing ☐

Food Intake:

Supplements ☐ Herbs ☐ Water ☐ Alcohol ☐ Tea ☐ Coffee ☐

Light ☐ Heavy ☐ Nourishing ☐

Breakfast: ________

Mid Day – Biggest Meal of the Day: ________

Supper/Dinner: ________

Environment:

Happy ☐ Stressful ☐ Peaceful ☐ Quiet ☐

PM Activities:

Cooking ☐ Laundry ☐ Walk ☐ Workout ☐
De-cluttering ☐ Meditation ☐ Oil Massage ☐ Yoga ☐
Bath ☐ Journaling ☐ Reading ☐ Chatting ☐
Computer ☐ Music ☐ TV ☐ Movies ☐

Other: ________

Bed Time:

Foot massage ☐ Reading ☐ Meditation ☐

Other: ________

NADI PARIKSHA

AYURVEDIC PULSE DIAGNOSIS

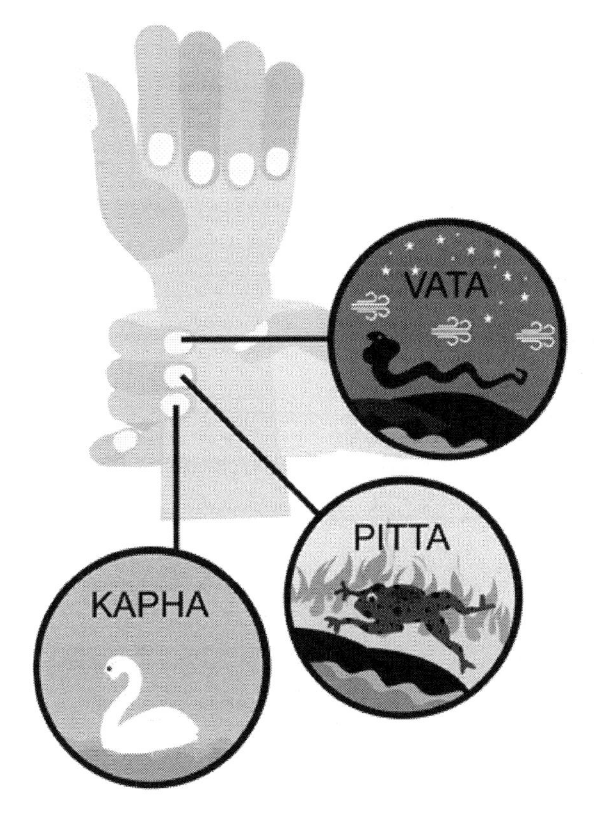

READ YOUR PULSE TO DETERMINE YOUR DOSHA.

Each finger corresponds to a specific dosha—the index finger to Vata, the middle finger to Pitta, and the ring finger to Kapha. Feel for the location of the force within the pulse and under which finger you feel it the strongest. The topmost layer will be your Vikruti (current condition), and the deepest layer your Prakruti (born constitution).

Every person is subjected to the constant interaction with his or her environment, which will affect the person's constitution at any time. Ayurveda teaches that your Vikruti can be changed by following your daily routines, so as to approach your Prakruti or the state where you have perfect health.

JIHVA PARIKSHA

AYURVEDIC TONGUE DIAGNOSIS

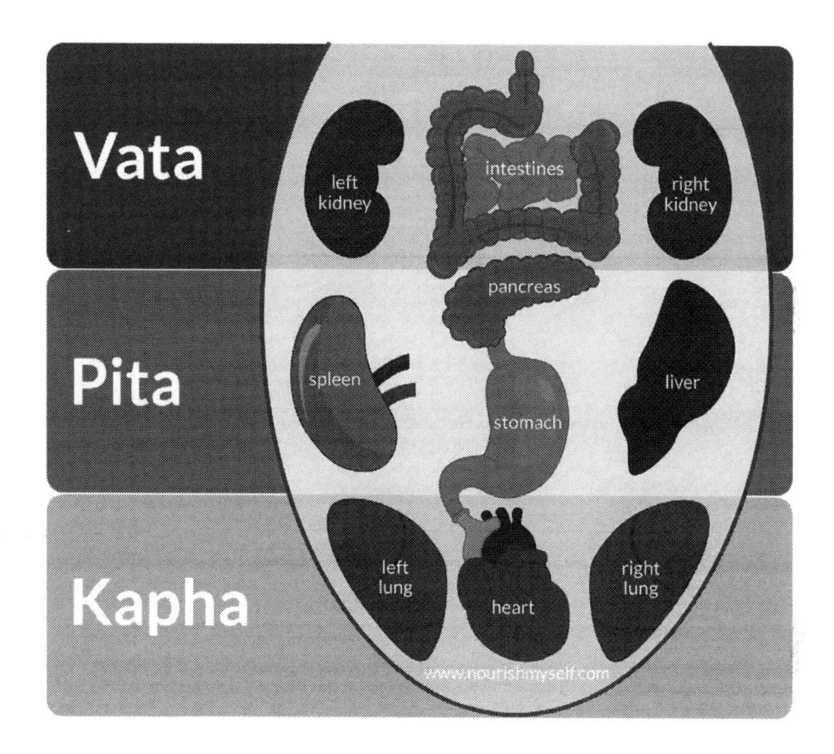

THE TONGUE DOES NOT LIE!

In Ayurveda, the tongue is used as an investigative tool for determining our state of health. The tongue is the very beginning of the digestive tract. Since we can not see much beyond the mouth, a quick look at the tongue can tell us much about the health of our inner digestive system.

12 MOST ESSENTIAL HERBS/SPICES FOR YOUR HOME

immune - respiratory - headaches - sinus - lungs

gastric pains - arthritis

mental clarity - depression - rheumatism

digestion - respiratory

organ cleanser - digestion

tonic for liver - digestion

digestion - cramps - gas

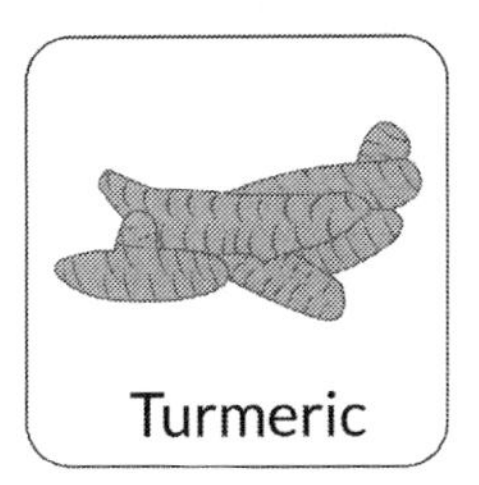

immune builder - arthritis - anti bacterial - anti inflammatory

strengthens heart/lungs - digestion - circulation

circulation - digestion - congestion

digestion - congestion - circulation

mental clarity - blood cleanser - congestion

12 MOST ESSENTIAL OILS FOR YOUR HOME

Holy Basil

congestion - clarity

Rose

emotional balance - cell regenerator

Frankincense

anti inflammatory - antiseptic

Helichrysum

lymph - skin

Tea Tree

anti bacterial - respiratory

Lavender

balancing - insomnia

Lemon

digestion - anxiety

Camomile

skin - insomnia

Neem

antiseptic - antifungal

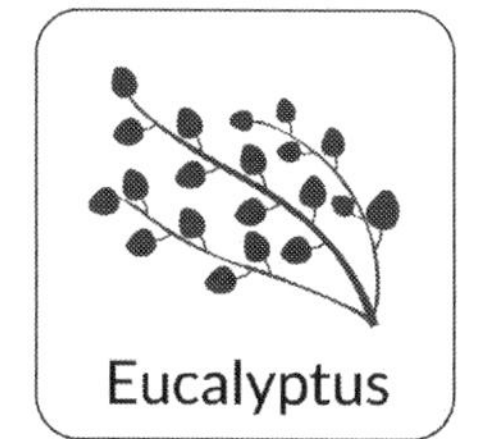

Eucalyptus

decongestant - disinfects the air

Rosemary

pain relief - memory - hair growth

Sandalwood

circulation - mental health

YOGA POSES

January

Tree Pose - Vrksasana
balance, stability, self-confidence

February

Boat Pose - Navasana
stimulates organs, digestion, relieves stress

March

Chair Pose - Utkatasana
stimulates heart, abdominal organs, tones, strengthens

April

Seated Twist - Marichyasana 111
calms nervous system, constipation, digestion, fatigue

May

Bridge Pose - Setu Bandha Sarvangasana
circulation, digestion, anxiety, insomnia

June

Cobra - Bhujangasana
elevates mood, invigorates heart, stress, fatigue

July

Side Plank - Vashithasana
balance, stability, strength, coordination

August

Child's Pose - Balasana
circulation, calms mind/body, anxiety, encourages breath

September

Legs up the wall - Viparita Karani
depression, insomnia, circulation, restores tired feet legs

October

Supported Shoulder Stand - Sarvangasana
respiratory, oxygen to organs, digestion, blood flow

November

Head to knee Pose - Janu Sirasana
calms brain, depression, stimulates organs, headaches, fatigue

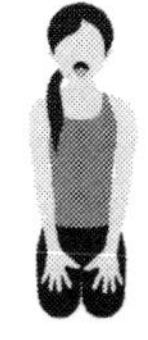

December

Lion Pose - Simhasana
tension, circulation, respiratory, stimulates nerves

www.nourishmyself.com

Sun Salutation sequences are often done to awaken the body and create energy and heat. The salute to the sun is a dynamic sequence of poses which on a physical level builds stamina and strength and connects movement with breath. On a more symbolic level the sequence offers gratitude to the sun, the energy and light it provides for all of life on earth.

Moon Salutation sequences are often done to cool and soothe the body. They are especially nice to do in the evening as the meditative, calming quality of the poses helps to form an easy connection to the breath, preparing the body and the mind for a restful night's sleep.

CHAKRAS

The 7 swirling wheels of energy in our bodies, where matter and consciousness meet to keep us healthy and vibrant.

Crown - Sahaswara Chakra
I am Divine

Third Eye - Ajna Chakra
I am Connected

Throat - Vishuddha Chakra
I am Expressive

Heart - Anahata Chakra
I am Loved

Solar Plexus - Manipura Chakra
I am Strong

Sacral - Svadhisthana Chakra
I am Creative

Root - Muladhara Chakra
I am Safe

MUDRAS - HAND GESTURES

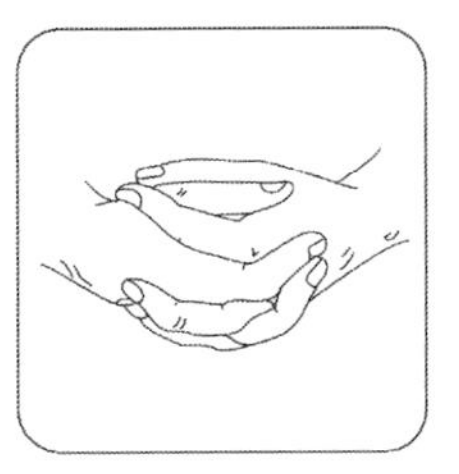

Brahma
Ushas Mudra
Creativity & pleasure

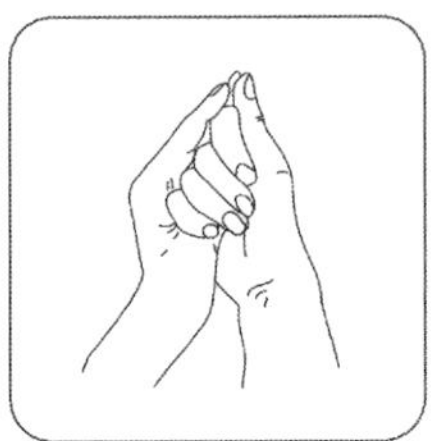

Radha Krishna
Shankha Mudra
Cures throat problems

Lord Shiva
Linga Mudra
Surge of energy

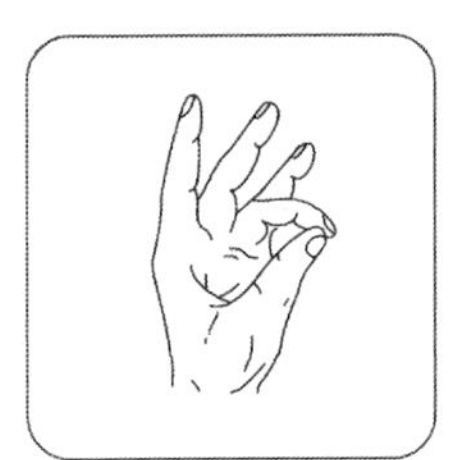

Goddess Sita
Prithvi Mudra
Stability & strength

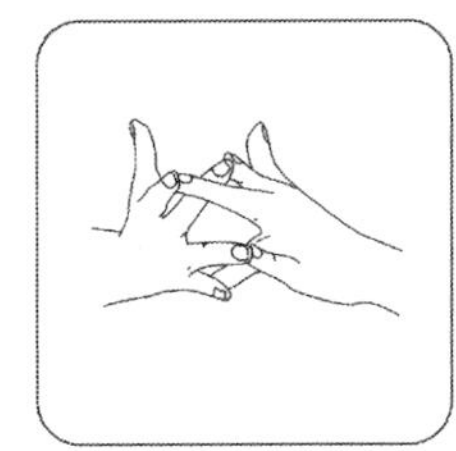

Ma Yashoda
Surabhi Mudra
Balance five body elements

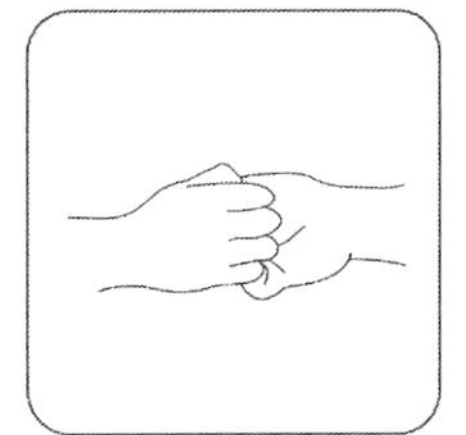

Lord Ganesha
Ganesh Mudra
Overcome obstacles

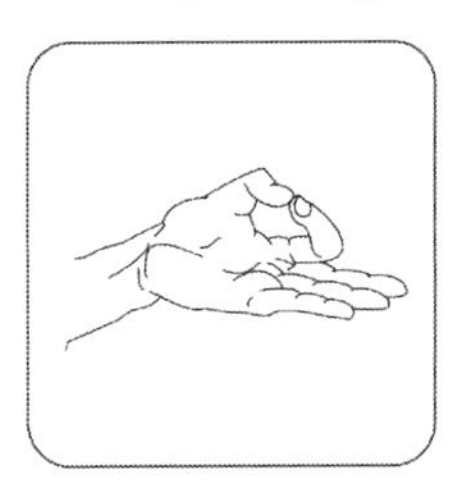

Goddess Saraswati
Gyana Mudra
Spiritual progress

Goddess Ganga
Varuna Mudra
Balancing water element

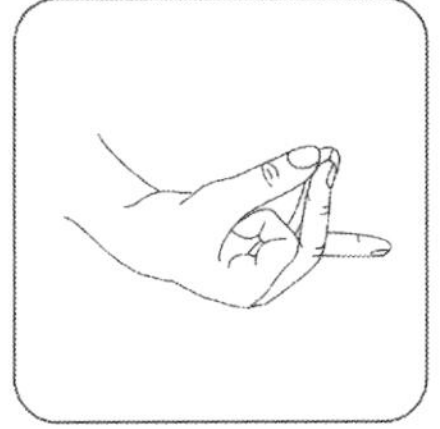

Lord Dhanwantari
Apan Vayu Mudra
Mitigates heart disease

Goddess Durga
Shakti Mudra
Peace & serenity

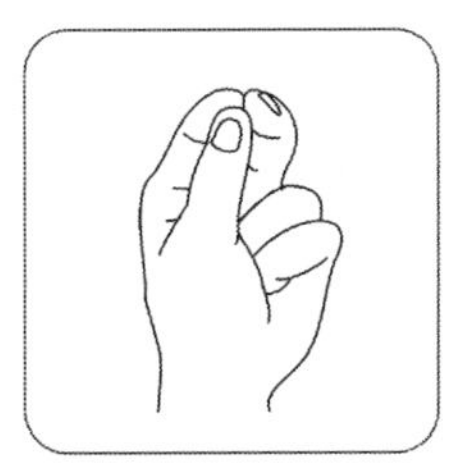

Goddess Lakshmi
Kubera Mudra
Desires & wealth

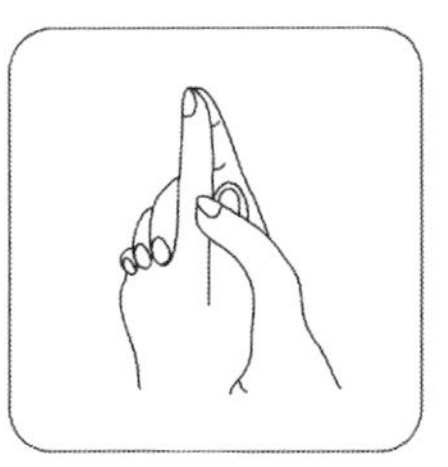

Goddess Kali
Ksepana Mudra
Destruction & transformation

RECIPES

OILS FOR STEAM INHALATION OR DIFFUSING

COLDS **Two drops**	FLU **One drop**	SINUS **One drop**	COUGH **One drop**	FEVER **Two drops**	HEADACHES **Two drops**
Eucalyptus	Thyme	Elemi	Hyssop	Lavender	Eucalyptus
Rosemary	Cajeput	Eucalyptus	Sage		Camphor
Camphor		Cypress	Anise	**One drop**	Lavender
		Neroli	Sandalwood	Camomile	Ginger
		Yarrow			Cajeput
		Inula			Bergamot
		Tea tree			Tea tree
		Rosemary			Peppermint
					Geranium

SELF-MASSAGE (ABYANGHA) OIL

	VATA	PITTA	KAPHA
Base Oil	Organic Sesame Oil , Jojoba Oil or Avocado Oil	Organic fractionated Coconut Oil or Jojoba Oil	Organic Almond Oil or Avocado Oil or Flax Oil
Essential Oils	geranium, lavender, ylang ylang, rose, frankincense, cedarwood, rosewood, vanilla, camomile, tulsi, eucalyptus	camomile, sandalwood, lavender, helichrysm, rose, lemongrass, bergamot, peppermint, clary sage, jasmine, vetiver, gardenia, neem, vanilla	rosemary, eucalyptus, tulsi, clary sage, juniper, neroli, orange, thyme jatamasi, cypress, sandalwood, oregano, peppermint, rose, sage, champa, tea tree

Pick your favorite essential oils. **Always dilute essential oils.** 15–20 drops in 1 oz vegetable oil of your choice suggested for your body type.

COCONUT OIL PULLING BLEND

- 4 oz. fractionated Organic Coconut Oil
- 10 drops Organic Anise or Fennel oil
- 10 drops Organic Peppermint Oil
- 2 drops Organic Clove Oil (for cavities)
- 4 oz. glass bottle

Mix all the ingredients in a glass bottle. Shake to mix. Use a spoonful and swish and hold in your mouth for 10–20 minutes. Spit into a trash can. Not in your sink.

CCF TEA

- ½ tsp. Organic Cumin seeds
- ½ tsp. Organic Fennel seeds
- ½ tsp. Organic Coriander seeds

Bring 3 cups of water to boil add the cumin, coriander and fennel seeds. Simmer, strain and drink throughout the day. Cumin, coriander, and fennel are digestive spices, and when brewed together as a tea they make the perfect delight to an Ayurvedic lifestyle.

MOM'S DIGESTIVE CHEW

- Organic Ajwain seeds
- Organic Fennel seeds
- Organic Split Corriander seeds
- Black Salt

Roast seeds in a skillet. Cool, put in a glass jar, and store. Add a pinch of black salt (kala namak) and eat a teaspoonful when you have digestive discomfort, like bloating and gas.

ORGANIC SPICE CHURNA MIX FOR OPTIMAL DIGESTION

VATA *(Warming/Calming)*	**PITTA** *(Cooling)*	**KAPHA** *(Stimulating)*
Cumin	Cumin	Ginger
Ginger	Coriander	Black Pepper
Cinnamon	Fennel	Turmeric
Fennel	Turmeric	Cumin
Lemon Peel	Cardamom	Coriander
Turmeric	Peppermint	Fenugreek
Hing		Cloves
Bay Leaf		Cinnamon
Ajwain		Oregano
Fenugreek		Thyme

Grind spices, put in an airtight container and keep in a cool place.

Cooking method: First heat oil or ghee then add the spice mix, cook for a few minutes until the aroma is released. Add to rice, steamed veggies or meat/fish dishes before serving or simply sprinkle on your food. Tip! Carry your spice mix with you when travelling.

GREEN IMMUNE SOUP (SERVES 8)

- 10 cups water
- ½ head of broccoli
- ½ head of cauliflower
- 5 stalks of celery
- ½ cup of green onions
- 1 bunch kale
- 1 cup cilantro
- ½ bulb of fennel
- 1 thumb size fresh turmeric
- 1 thumb size fresh ginger
- 4' piece of fresh burdock
- 2 sheets kombu
- 6 pieces of dried astragalus root
- 8 pieces (3" size) sulphur-free ashwagandha root
- 1 tsp. ajwain seeds
- 1 tsp. cumin seeds
- 1 tbs. coriander seeds
- 2 tbs. ghee

Saute spices in ghee, add chopped vegetables, add water. Bring to boil then simmer for about 1 ½ hours. Remove the hard stalks of astragalus, blend, strain and enjoy. Optional add miso (at the end), ghee, brags, lemon to taste. Garnish with cilantro.

OJAS BUILDING DRINK (ONE CUP)

- 1 cup raw whole organic milk, rice milk, almond milk, coconut milk or sesame milk
- 10 almonds, soaked overnight, peeled and chopped
- 2 whole dates, chopped
- ¼ teaspoon powdered organic ginger
- ¼ teaspoon powdered organic cardamom
- Pinch of organic turmeric
- Pinch of saffron

Place all ingredients in a saucepan. Bring to a low boil. If you like, use a frother to blend the mixture to a creamy consistency. Pour in a mug and Enjoy!

12 LOVING AFFIRMATIONS

I honor that life is filled with joy and abundance.

I am listening to my body, my mind, and my spirit's guidance.

I am detoxing and decluttering so I can reflect the light, the love, and the care I want for my mind and body connection.

I love all the tastes of nature. I am able to recognize all the elements working in my body allowing nature's gifts to bring me to perfect health.

I am powerful; therefore I believe I can be healthy, strong, clear, young, and vibrant.

I am breaking through my fears as I make positive changes.

I take action for everything in my life.

I am living a chemical-free life. I support organic farmers and love connecting with nature.

I let go of judgment of others and myself.

I tune myself with the rhythms of nature so I will have a transforming experience in my daily life.

I honor and respect my limitations and thank myself for the capabilities I have.

I am powerful, confident, and capable of reaching all my dreams.

AUSPICIOUS TOOLS OF THE GOD-GODDESS

Lotus Blossom
Purity, Liberation

River Ganga
Purity, Liberty

Veena
Art, Learning

Lotus Flower
Purity, Beauty

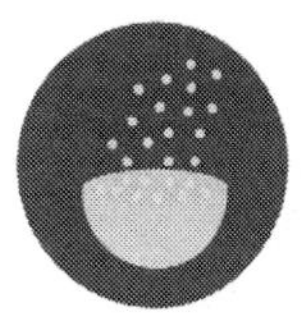

Gold Coin
Wealth, Abundance

Discus
Control over the World

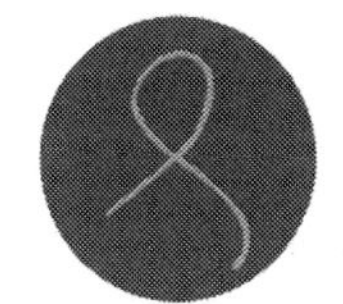

Rope
Focus on Goals

Book/Vedas
Knowledge, Learning

Mace
Cycle of Energy

Tiger
Courage Power

Damru (Drum)
Creation, Protection

Trident
Destroy evil, Ignorance

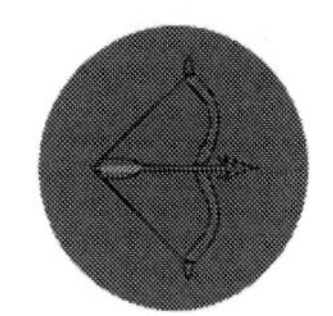

Bow & Arrow
Strength, Precision

Axe
Removal of Obstacles

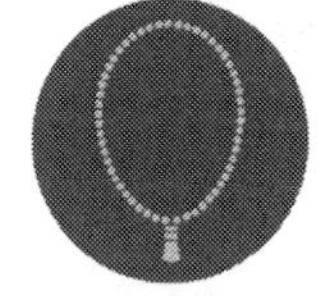

Beads
Prayer, Concentration

Sword
Mental Acuity

Water Jug
Purity, Fertility

Third eye
Burns Desires

Spear
Conquering Evil

AUSPICIOUS TOOLS OF THE GOD-GODDESS

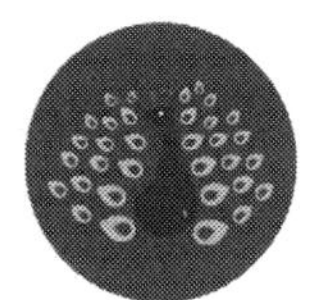

Peacock
Pride,
Arrogrance

Conch
Purity, Auspiciousness
Sound Om

Severed Head
Human Ego

Beards
Manhood,
Wisdom

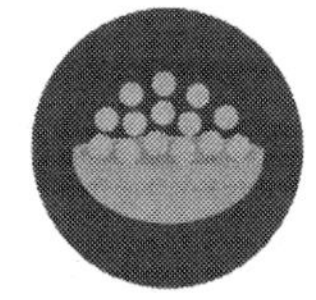

Laddu (Sweets)
Joy, Pleasure

Cobra
Spiritual
Energy

White Lotus
Rebirth

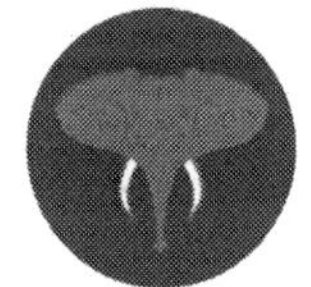

Elephant
Royalty
Strength

Rat
Desire
Freedom

White Swan
Purity, Grace

Owl
Wisdom
Brilliance

Crocodile
Dependability
Bravery

Thunderbolt
Strength, Firmness

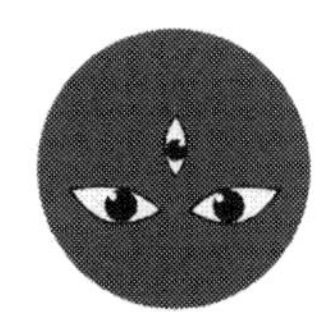

Three Eyes
Past, Present,
Future

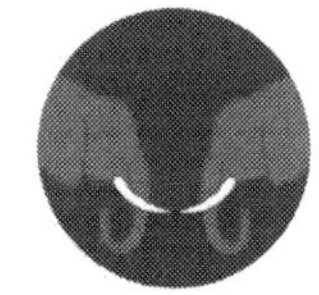

Two Elephants
Material, Spiritual
Prosperity

Crescent Moon
Measure of Time

Four Arms
Multiple Powers

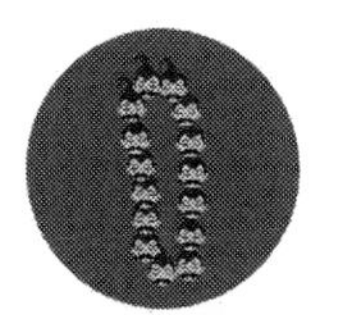

Skull/Head Necklace
Time, Immortality

MASTERY OF SELF-HABIT/ GOAL TRACKER

HABIT/GOAL	1	2	3	4	5	6	7	8	9	10	11	12	13	14	15	16	17	18	19	20	21	22	23	24	25	26	27	28	29	30	31

AYURVEDIC DAILY ROUTINE-DINACHARYA

THE ULTIMATE LIFESTYLE FOR GOOD HEALTH & WELLBEING

Living our day in sync with Nature's Rhythms is the key factor which can determine our optimal health and build resistance to disease. Follow this daily sequence and notice your transformation.

MORNING

- Wake up early, before sunrise
- Drink 1–2 cups of warm water
- Wash face/mouth/eyes
- Scrape tongue/brush teeth
- Gargle/Oil Pull
- Eliminate
- Apply oil to nostrils (Nasya)
- Dry brush skin
- Self-Massage (Abhyanga), before or after shower
- 5–10 minutes of breathing exercise (Pranayama)
- Meditate/sit in silence
- Exercise for 20 minutes (yoga, walk, run)
- Breakfast: Juice, fruit, herbal tea. Warm grains or protein if hungry.

MID-DAY

- Eat largest meal
- Incorporate all 6 tastes at each meal: sweet, sour, salty, bitter, pungent, astringent
- Reduce rushing/worrying
- Be kind/loving/playful
- Power nap on left side
- Connect with Nature

EVENING

- Quit work by 6 p.m.
- Eat an early light dinner
- Sit and eat with awareness
- Engage in activities that brings you joy
- Power off all electronics by 7 p.m.
- Journal
- Massage feet
- Meditate
- Bed by 10 p.m.

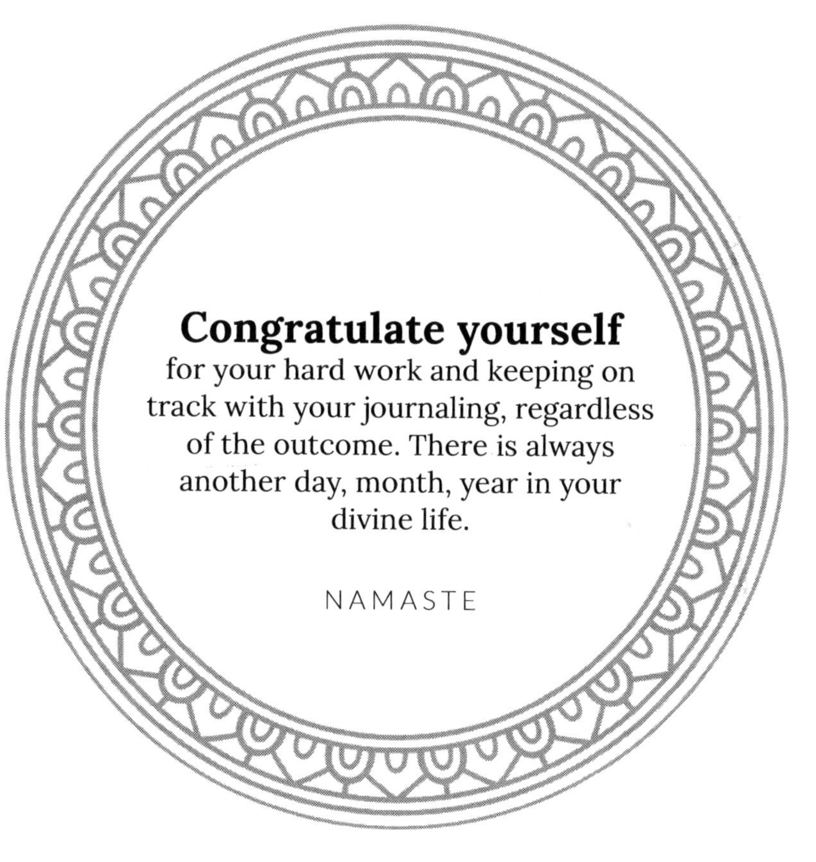

Congratulate yourself
for your hard work and keeping on track with your journaling, regardless of the outcome. There is always another day, month, year in your divine life.

NAMASTE

“

May you honor the peace that lies deep within your heart ... and may you always connect to the radiant light that surrounds you and protects you ... and with each step you take upon our mother earth may you understand your ability to heal our earth, yourself and all those who cross your path.

SAT NAM
JIWAN KAUR

DOWNLOAD YOUR FREE WORKBOOK

The workbook has printable pages for you to keep track of your progress.

www.thedivinitywithinjournal.com

Resources, Essential Oils & Ayurvedic Suppliers:
Goddess Oils available from Dr. Light Miller at www.ayurvedichealers.com

Lab of Flowers. www.labofflowers.com
The Ayurvedic Institute. www.ayurveda.com
Banyan Botanicals. www.banyanbotanicals.com
Maharishi Ayurveda. www.mapi.com

BATOOL MERALI

Batool Merali is an Ayurvedic Lifestyle Practitioner and yoga teacher. She guides people to thrive in body, mind, and spirit: releasing the anxiety that is holding them back in reaching their highest potential and to experience the magic of life.

She spent her early years raising two fine boys and working with her husband at his successful business. Our modern hectic lifestyle, while very gratifying, leaves one with no time, high amounts of stress, and depleted energy.

Going back to her roots, she found Ayurveda. Health and beauty begins from within. She teaches thoughtful and practical application of yoga, Ayurveda, and kitchen medicine to evolve, transform, and lead you to a vibrant, graceful, ageless life.

Batool is a certified Ayurvedic practitioner through NAMA (The National Ayurvedic Medical Association) & APPANA (Association of Ayurvedic Professionals of North America), Certified Yoga Health Coach with Yogahealer LLC, as well as a RYT 500 Yoga Alliance teacher.

Her college studies began in London, then California where she graduated with a bachelor's in Art & Design, a bachelor's of Science, in Divinity and Ayurveda, from the Ayurvedic College of Wellbeing in Florida. She calls herself a student for life, continually studying with Dr. Vasant Lad, Dr. Frawley, Dr. Suhas and others.

She lives in Rapid City, South Dakota and in Miami, Florida. In Florida, she worked at the Pancha Karma Clinic with Dr. Light Miller. She teaches online and does Skype consultations for those that cannot meet in person.

WWW.NOURISHMYSELF.COM

VIDYA LIGHT MILLER

Vidya Light Miller, ND, DD, received her BS in social science from UC Berkeley, became a Certified Massage Therapist at the LA School of Massage in 1967, and has since acquired over 44 years of experience as a health practitioner.

In addition to providing individual health counseling and teaching seminars, Light has trained and certified over 500 massage therapists. She is currently the only woman out of the 18 practitioners of Kaya Kalpa in the world. Kaya Kalpa is a branch of Ayurvedic Mystical Medicine, the oldest recorded healing art.

Light has been ordained as a minister since 1983. Her vision and her ministry is based on bringing awareness of health and spirituality to everyone that crosses her path. She teaches meditation, self-development courses, and helps people to find their passion and purpose in life. She received her Doctor of Divinity and has followed her mission ever since.

Drs. Bryan and Light Miller own the Ayurvedic College of Wellbeing, teaching online and in person. Their Online Education Program is the only one of its kind on the East Coast.

They have recently moved to Rincon, Puerto Rico. Vidya Light Miller offers Pancha Karma treatments, Ayurvedic consultations, Kaya Kalpa, Tarpana, Shirodhara, Indian Massage, Lymphatic Massage, Colimas, and many more services.

WWW.AYURVEDICHEALERS.COM

Made in the USA
Lexington, KY
17 September 2017